California Science

PEARSON
Scott Foresman

Grade 1 Teacher's Edition • Unit B
Editorial Offices: Glenview, Illinois • Parsippany, New Jersey • New York, New York
Sales Offices: Boston, Massachusetts • Duluth, Georgia • Glenview, Illinois • Coppell, Texas •
Sacramento, California • Mesa, Arizona

ISBN: 0-328-24124-5
This product may appear as part of package ISBN: 0-328-24134-2.

1 2 3 4 5 6 7 8 9 10 V003 13 12 11 10 09 08 07 06

Series Authors

Dr. Olga Amaral
Chair, Division of Teacher Education
San Diego State University
Calexico, California

Dr. Timothy Cooney
Professor of Earth Science and Science Education
University of Northern Iowa (UNI)
Cedar Falls, Iowa

Dr. Jim Cummins
Professor
Department of Curriculum, Teaching, and Learning
University of Toronto
Toronto, Canada

Dr. James Flood
Distinguished Professor of Literacy and Language
School of Teacher Education
San Diego State University
San Diego, California

Barbara Kay Foots, M.Ed.
Science Education Consultant
Houston, Texas

Dr. M. Jenice Goldston
Associate Professor of Science Education
Department of Elementary Education Programs
University of Alabama
Tuscaloosa, Alabama

Dr. Shirley Gholston Key
Associate Professor of Science Education
Instruction and Curriculum Leadership Department
College of Education
University of Memphis
Memphis, Tennessee

Dr. Diane Lapp
Distinguished Professor of Reading and Language Arts in Teacher Education
San Diego State University
San Diego, California

Sheryl A. Mercier
Classroom Teacher
Dunlap Elementary School
Dunlap, California

Dr. Karen L. Ostlund
Director
UTeach, College of Natural Sciences
The University of Texas at Austin
Austin, Texas

Dr. Nancy Romance
Professor of Science Education & Principal Investigator
NSF/IERI Science IDEAS Project
Charles E. Schmidt College of Science
Florida Atlantic University
Boca Raton, Florida

Dr. William Tate
Chair and Professor of Education and Applied Statistics
Department of Education
Washington University
St Louis, Missouri

Dr. Kathryn C. Thornton
Professor
School of Engineering and Applied Science
University of Virginia
Charlottesville, Virginia

Dr. Leon Ukens
Professor Emeritus
Department of Physics, Astronomy, and Geosciences
Towson University
Towson, Maryland

Steve Weinberg
Consultant
Connecticut Center for Advanced Technology
East Hartford, Connecticut

1 2 3 4 5 6 7 8 9 10 V057 15 14 13 12 11 10 09 08 07 06

Contributing Author

Dr. Michael P. Klentschy
Superintendent
El Centro Elementary School District
El Centro, California

Science Content Consultants

Dr. Herbert Brunkhorst
Chair
Department of Science,
Mathematics and Technology
College of Education
California State University, San Bernardino
San Bernardino, California

Dr. Karen Kolehmainen
Department of Physics
California State University, San Bernardino
San Bernardino, California

Dr. Stephen D Lewis
Earth and Environmental Sciences
California State University, Fresno
Fresno, California

NASA Content Consultants

Adena Williams Loston, Ph.D.
Chief Education Officer
Office of the Chief Education Officer

Clifford W. Houston, Ph.D.
Deputy Chief Education Officer for Education Programs
Office of the Chief Education Officer

Frank C. Owens
Senior Policy Advisor
Office of the Chief Education Officer

Deborah Brown Biggs
Manager, Education Flight Projects Office
Space Operations Mission Directorate, Education Lead

Erika G. Vick
NASA Liaison to Pearson Scott Foresman
Education Flight Projects Office

William E. Anderson
Partnership Manager for Education
Aeronautics Research Mission Directorate

Anita Krishnamurthi
Program Planning Specialist
Space Science Education and Outreach Program

Bonnie J. McClain
Chief of Education
Exploration Systems Mission Directorate

Diane Clayton, Ph.D.
Program Scientist
Earth Science Education

Deborah Rivera
Strategic Alliances Manager
Office of Public Affairs
NASA Headquarters

Douglas D. Peterson
*Public Affairs Office,
Astronaut Office*
Office of Public Affairs
NASA Johnson Space Center

Nicole Cloutier
*Public Affairs Office,
Astronaut Office*
Office of Public Affairs
NASA Johnson Space Center

iii

Reviewers

Elaine Chasse-DeMers
Teacher
Taylor Street School
Sacramento,
California

Kevin Clevenger
Teacher
Oak Chan
Elementary
Folsom, California

Kim Eddings
Teacher
Madison Elementary
Pomona, California

Joseph Frescatore
Teacher
Chavez Elementary
San Diego,
California

Candace Gibbons
Teacher
Freedom Elementary
Clovis, California

Anne Higginbotham
Teacher
Arundel Elementary
San Carlos,
California

Sean Higgins
Teacher
Monte Verde
Elementary
San Bruno,
California

Sharon Janulaw
Science Education
Specialist
Sonoma County
Office of Education
Santa Rosa,
California

Jeanne E. Martin
Teacher
John Gill School
Redwood City,
California

Mark Allen Schultz
Teacher
Theodore Judah
Elementary
Folsom, California

Corinne Schwartz
Teacher
Lincrest Elementary
Yuba City,
California

Schelly T. Solko
Teacher
Loudon School
Bakersfield,
California

Kevin Soulé
Instructional
Specialist
Alhambra USD
Alhambra,
California

Bobbie Stumbaugh
Teacher
Roy Cloud School
Redwood City,
California

Kimberly Thiesen
Teacher
Freedom Elementary
Clovis, California

Carole Bialek Vargas
Teacher
Empire Oaks
Elementary
Folsom, California

Bonita J. Walker-Davis
Teacher
Don Riggio School
Stockton, California

Debra Willsie
Teacher
Tarpey Elementary
Clovis, California

Olivia Winslow
Teacher
Earl Warren
Elementary
Sacramento,
California

California
Science

v

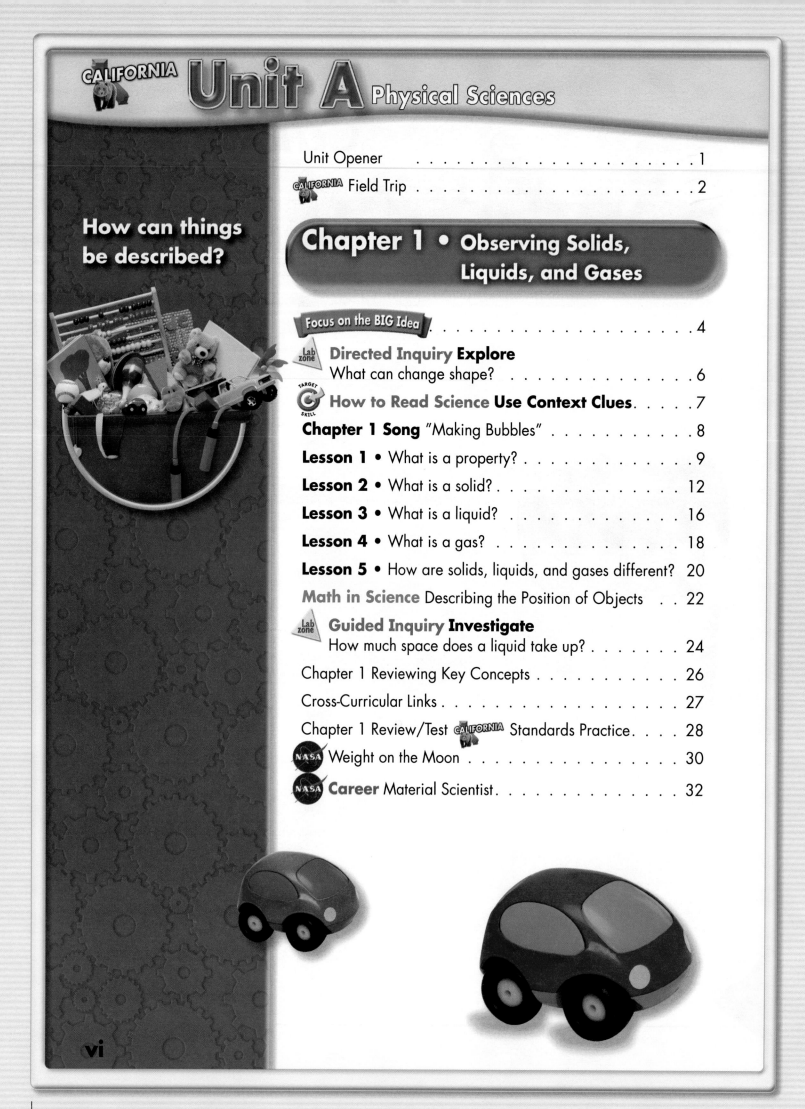

Chapter 2 • Changing Solids, Liquids, and Gases

How can things be changed?

What do plants and animals need?

Chapter 3 • Needs of Plants and Animals

Where do plants and animals live?

Chapter 4 • Environments

Chapter 5 • Plants and Animals Living Together

How do plants and animals live together?

How can you tell about the weather?

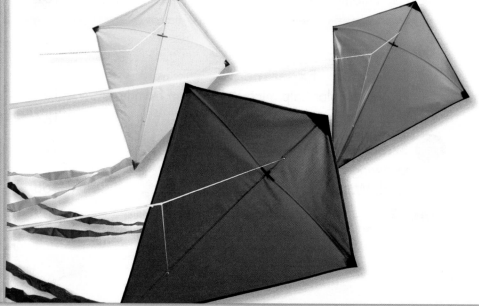

Chapter 7 • Seasons

What is the weather like in different seasons?

CALIFORNIA
Unit B

Life Sciences

Malibu Creek State Park

1LS2.0 Plants and animals meet their needs in different ways.

More Facts About Malibu Creek State Park

Malibu Creek State Park is a large wilderness area very close to a large urban center. The following facts about Malibu Creek State Park and its varied habitats can be found on the California State Park Web site.

▶ The park is home to many animals and birds.

▶ The park has over 4,000 acres of varied habitat.

▶ Malibu Creek, the principal watercourse of the Santa Monica mountains, runs for 25 miles through the park. It provides water for the many animals who live in the park.

▶ Some of the land is covered with oak and sycamore woodlands. These provide food for squirrels, raccoons, skunks, and deer.

▶ Land that is now in the park was the ancestral home of the Chumash Native Americans.

▶ Malibu Creek State Park has been used to film scenes from TV shows and movies.

California Field Trip

Malibu Creek State Park

Los Angeles, California

Malibu Creek State Park is only 25 miles from Los Angeles. It is in the middle of the Santa Monica Mountains. Many birds, insects, and other animals find food and shelter in the park.

Find Out More

Research to find out more about this Malibu Creek State Park.

● Make a list of some plants and animals you can see at the park.

Los Angeles

72

─ Visual Arts Link ─

Provide children with modeling clay. Ask children to choose one of the animals from their list. Invite children to make sculptures of the animals they chose. Allow volunteers to discuss their sculptures with the class.

Integrate Your Day

▶ Educationally relevant cross-curricular ideas are integrated into science lessons.

▶ Children practice mathematics, aligned with the *Mathematics Framework for California Public Schools.*

▶ Children practice reading and writing expository text, aligned with the *Reading-Language Arts Framework for California Public Schools.*

Mathematics Standards	Page number
1NS1.1 Number Sense Count, read, and write whole numbers to 100.	157
1NS1.2 Number Sense Compare and order whole numbers to 100 by using the symbols for less than, equal to, or greater than (<, =, >).	141
1NS1.3 Number Sense Represent equivalent forms of the same number through the use of physical models, diagrams, and number expressions (to 20) (e.g., 8 may be represented as 4 + 4, 5 + 3, 2 + 2 + 2 + 2, 10 − 2, 11 − 3).	93
1NS2.1 Number Sense Know the addition facts (sums to 20) and the corresponding subtraction facts and commit them to memory.	123
1MG2.4 Measurement and Geometry Arrange and describe objects in space by proximity, position, and direction (e.g., near, far, below, above, up, down, behind, in front of, next to, left or right of).	83, 111
1PS1.1 Statistics, Data Analysis, and Probability Sort objects and data by common attributes and describe the categories.	152–153
1PS1.2 Statistics, Data Analysis, and Probability Represent and compare data (e.g., largest, smallest, most often, least often) by using pictures, bar graphs, tally charts, and picture graphs.	88–89, 118–119

English-Language Arts Standards	Page number
1RW1.0 Word Analysis, Fluency, and Systematic Vocabulary Development Students understand the basic features of reading. They select letter patterns and know how to translate them into spoken language by using phonics, syllabication, and word parts. They apply this knowledge to achieve fluent oral and silent reading.	74–75, 98–99, 128–129
1RW1.1 Word Analysis, Fluency, and Systematic Vocabulary Development Match oral words to printed words.	107
1RW1.16 Word Analysis, Fluency, and Systematic Vocabulary Development Read aloud with fluency in a manner that sounds like natural speech.	96, 126, 160–161, 162
1RW1.17 Word Analysis, Fluency, and Systematic Vocabulary Development Classify grade-appropriate categories of words (e.g., concrete collections of animals, foods, toys).	133
1RC2.4 Reading Comprehension Use context to resolve ambiguities about word and sentence meanings.	101, 103
1RC2.5 Reading Comprehension Confirm predictions about what will happen next in a text by identifying key words (i.e., signpost words).	79, 131
1RC2.6 Reading Comprehension Relate prior knowledge to textual information.	77
1RC2.7 Reading Comprehension Retell the central ideas of simple expository or narrative passages.	145, 149
1WS1.1 Writing Strategies Select a focus when writing.	84, 112, 146
1WS1.2 Writing Strategies Use descriptive words when writing.	104
1WA2.1 Writing Applications Write brief narratives (e.g., fictional, autobiographical) describing an experience.	80, 123
1WA2.2 Writing Applications Write brief expository descriptions of a real object, person, place, or event, using sensory details.	93, 108, 116, 134, 150
1WOL1.1 Written and Oral English Language Conventions Write and speak in complete, coherent sentences.	123, 142, 157
1WOL1.2 Written and Oral English Language Conventions Identify and correctly use singular and plural nouns.	115

Reading Support

▶ **Focus on the Big Idea,** SE/TE pp. 74–75, 98–99, 128–129

▶ ⊘ **Relate Prior Knowledge,** SE/TE pp. 77, 81, 83, 95

▶ ⊘ **Use Context Clues,** SE/TE pp. 101, 105, 107, 125

▶ ⊘ **Predict,** SE/TE pp. 131, 139, 147, 159

▶ **English-Language Arts Support,** TE pp. 77, 79, 101, 103, 107, 131, 133, 145, 149

History-Social Science Link

▶ **California State Animal,** SE/TE p. 157

Writing Support

▶ ✎ **Writing in Science** SE/TE pp. 85, 94, 109, 117, 124, 135, 137, 149, 158

▶ **Building Vocabulary,** SE/TE pp. 93, 123, 157

▶ **English-Language Arts Support,** TE p. 115

▶ **Write About Science,** TE pp. 80, 84, 104, 108, 112, 116, 134, 142, 146, 150

▶ **Living in a Desert,** TE p. 123

Mathematics Support

▶ **Mathematics Support,** TE pp. 83, 89, 111, 119, 141, 153

▶ **Math in Science,** SE/TE pp. 88–89, 118–119, 152–153

▶ **Planning a Garden,** SE/TE p. 93

▶ **Numbering Wolves,** SE/TE p. 123

▶ **Counting Teeth,** SE/TE p. 157

Health Links

▶ **Eating Vegetables,** SE/TE p. 93

▶ **Staying Safe in the Sun,** SE/TE p. 123

Technology Links

▶ **NSTA SciLinks,** SE/TE pp. 83, 111, 139

▶ **Discovery Channel School DVD**

▶ Children may access the Online Student Edition at **www.sfsuccessnet.com**.

Visual and Performing Arts Links

▶ **Visual Arts Link,** TE p. 72

▶ **Drawing a Leaf,** SE/TE p. 93

▶ **Food Chain Play,** SE/TE p. 157

FOR TEACHERS

| PLAN | TEACH | ASSESS |

CHAPTER 3 — Needs of Plants and Animals

Discovery Channel School Professional Development Video
Characteristics of Living Things

Printable Resources
- *Science Study Notebook* pp. 31–42
  - Vocabulary Cards
- *Intervention Study Guide* pp. 22–27
- *Assessment Book* pp. 31–40
- *Teacher's Activity Guide* pp. 16–17
- *Chapter 3 Content Readers*
- *Graphic Organizers* TE pp. EMxix–EMxxv
- *Letter Home* TE pp. EMvii–EMviii
- *Student Standards Progress Report* TE pp. EMxvii–EMxviii

Activity Video
- *Do plants need water?*
- *Do plants need light?*

Content Reader Database Support
- *Needs of Plants and Animals*
- *Plants and Animals*
- *What We Need*

Success Tracker
- *Chapter 3 Digital Assessment*
- *Chapter 3 Digital Targeted Resources*

ExamView
- *Customizable Chapter 3 Test*

CHAPTER 4 — Environments

Discovery Channel School Professional Development Video
Ecological Organization

Printable Resources
- *Science Study Notebook* pp. 43–55
  - Vocabulary Cards
- *Intervention Study Guide* pp. 28–35
- *Assessment Book* pp. 41–50
- *Teacher's Activity Guide* pp. 18–19
- *Chapter 4 Content Readers*
- *Graphic Organizers* TE pp. EMxix–EMxxv
- *Letter Home* TE pp. EMix–EMx
- *Student Standards Progress Report* TE pp. EMxvii–EMxviii

Activity Video
- *Where do animals live?*
- *How do some desert leaves hold water?*

Content Reader Database Support
- *Environments*
- *Different Environments*
- *Swamp Life*

Success Tracker
- *Chapter 4 Digital Assessment*
- *Chapter 4 Digital Targeted Resources*

ExamView
- *Customizable Chapter 4 Test*

CHAPTER 5 — Plants and Animals Living Together

Discovery Channel School Professional Development Video
Ecological Organization

Printable Resources
- *Science Study Notebook* pp. 57–73
  - Vocabulary Cards
- *Intervention Study Guide* pp. 36–47
- *Assessment Book* pp. 51–66
- *Teacher's Activity Guide* pp. 20–22
- *Chapter 5 Content Readers*
- *Graphic Organizers* TE pp. EMxix–EMxxv
- *Letter Home* TE pp. EMxi–EMxii
- *Student Standards Progress Report* TE pp. EMxvii–EMxviii

Activity Video
- *What do animals eat for food?*
- *How can you make a model of a food chain?*
- *How can color help mice stay hidden from hawks?*

Content Reader Database Support
- *Plants and Animals Living Together*
- *Animals and Plants Live Together*
- *Life in the Bay*

Success Tracker
- *Chapter 5 Digital Assessment*
- *Chapter 5 Digital Targeted Resources*

ExamView
- *Customizable Chapter 5 Test*

FOR STUDENTS

| READ | REINFORCE | PRACTICE |

CHAPTER 3 — Needs of Plants and Animals

 DIGITAL **Online Student Edition**
Chapter 3 Needs of Plants and Animals

 DIGITAL **Content Reader Database Support**
▶ *Needs of Plants and Animals*
▶ *Plants and Animals*
▶ *What We Need*

DIGITAL **Active Art**
What Makes Plants Grow?

VIDEO **Discovery Channel School Student Video**
Social Insects

DIGITAL **SciLinks**
keyword: **roots**
code: **gr1p83**

DIGITAL **Web Game**
Food Chains

DIGITAL **eTools**
Counters

DIGITAL **LabZone Activities**
LabZone Activities are available for the Directed Inquiry Activity and Guided Inquiry Activity in Chapter 3. These science activities can be done along with, or in place of, the inquiry activities in the Student Edition.

DIGITAL **Active Glossary**
living   roots
nutrients   leaves

DIGITAL **MindPoint QuizShow**
▶ *Chapter 3 review in game format*

CHAPTER 4 — Environments

 DIGITAL **Online Student Edition**
Chapter 4 Environments

 DIGITAL **Content Reader Database Support**
▶ *Environments*
▶ *Different Environments*
▶ *Swamp Life*

DIGITAL **Active Art**
Ocean Plants and Animals

VIDEO **Discovery Channel School Student Video**
Temperate Rain Forest

DIGITAL **SciLinks**
keyword: **ocean**
code: **gr1p110**

DIGITAL **Web Game**
North American Biomes

DIGITAL **eTools**
Spreadsheet/Data/Grapher

DIGITAL **LabZone Activities**
LabZone Activities are available for the Directed Inquiry Activity and Guided Inquiry Activity in Chapter 4. These science activities can be done along with, or in place of, the inquiry activities in the Student Edition.

DIGITAL **Active Glossary**
environment   forest
ocean   desert

DIGITAL **MindPoint QuizShow**
▶ *Chapter 4 review in game format*

CHAPTER 5 — Plants and Animals Living Together

 DIGITAL **Online Student Edition**
Chapter 5 Plants and Animals Living Together

 DIGITAL **Content Reader Database Support**
▶ *Plants and Animals Living Together*
▶ *Animals and Plants Live Together*
▶ *Life in the Bay*

DIGITAL **Active Art**
Food Chain

VIDEO **Discovery Channel School Student Video**
Bees

DIGITAL **SciLinks**
keyword: **food chains**
code: **gr1p138**

DIGITAL **Web Game**
Food Web

DIGITAL **eTools**
Geometry Shapes

DIGITAL **LabZone Activities**
LabZone Activities are available for the Directed Inquiry Activity and Guided Inquiry Activity in Chapter 5, as well as for the Full Inquiry Activity at the end of Unit B. These science activities can be done along with, or in place of, the inquiry activities in the Student Edition.

DIGITAL **Active Glossary**
shelter   food chain
marsh

DIGITAL **MindPoint QuizShow**
▶ *Chapter 5 review in game format*

Reading Resources

	Easy	Average	Challenge

CHAPTER 3

Needs of Plants and Animals

A Polar Bear Can Swim
by Harriet Ziefret
(Puffin, ISBN 0-14-038692-0)

Circle-story picture book shows the different abilities of various animals.

What Plants and Animals Need
by Nancy Leber
(Compass Point Books, ISBN 0-75650-629-1)

A 16-page controlled-vocabulary book describes the needs of plants and animals.

Frogs, Toads, Lizards, and Salamanders
by Nancy Winslow Parker
(Greenwillow Books, ISBN 0-68808-681-0)

Humorous verses discuss the physical characteristics, behavior, habitats, and life cycles of these animals.

CHAPTER 4

Environments

Under One Rock: Bugs, Slugs, and Other Ughs
by Anthony D. Fredericks
(Dawn Publications, ISBN 1-58469-027-5)

Easy-reader book encourages children to see the wildlife hidden in their environment.

Where Once There Was a Wood
by Denise Fleming
(Henry Holt and Co., ISBN 0-80506-482-6)

This 32-page environmentally conscious, poetic picture book deals with the loss of habitats and how children can respond.

Storm on the Desert
by Carolyn Lesser
(Harcourt Children's Books, ISBN 0-15272-198-3)

Introduces desert environment, wildlife, and weather. Shows the dynamic, changing nature of environments.

CHAPTER 5

Plants and Animals Living Together

Hungry Animals: My First Look at a Food Chain
by Pamela Hickman
(Kids Can Press, ISBN 1-55074-204-3)

A short introduction to the food chain using simple words and highly supportive illustrations.

Who Eats What? Food Chains and Food Webs
by Patricia Lauber
(HarperCollins, ISBN 0-06445-130-5)

The food chain is illustrated and the application to people is shown.

What Do You Do When Something Wants to Eat You?
by Steve Jenkins
(Houghton Mifflin, ISBN 0-39582-514-8)

Illustrates both the food chain and how animal parts help animals live and grow.

Professional Development Resources

▶ **Classroom Creature Culture**
by Carol Hampton, et al.
(National Science Teachers Association Press, ISBN 0-87355-120-6)

An anthology about collecting, investigating, and caring for plants and animals in the classroom. Supports teaching ecological awareness and respect for life.

▶ **Science Knowledge and the Environment**
by Michael Littledyke, et al.
(Taylor and Francis Group, ISBN 1-85346-625-5)

This 180-page book draws inspiration from Rachel Carson and can be used throughout the primary science curriculum.

▶ **The Oxford Children's Encyclopedia of Plants and Animals, New Ed.**
(Oxford Univ. Press, ISBN 0-19-910777-7)

This 128-page introduction to living things has 140 main entries and 250 full-color photos and drawings.

▶ **Bottle Biology**
by Mrill Ingram
(Kendall/Hunt Publishing, ISBN 0-8403-8601-X)

Details suggestions for using bottles and cans to model full ecosystem gardens and decomposition. Also available in Spanish.

Classroom Equipment Kit

	Activities	School-supplied materials	Kit materials
CHAPTER 3	**Do plants need water?** p. 76	water	clear plastic deli bowls aquarium gravel pinto bean seeds magnifier
	Do plants need light? pp. 90–91	water pouring container washable paints (optional)	clear plastic cups grass seeds potting soil
CHAPTER 4	**Where do animals live?** p. 100	unruled index cards	animal picture cards yarn
	How do some desert leaves hold water? pp. 120–121	Desert Leaf Shapes (Activity Master 1) green construction paper water plate or tray (optional)	spray bottle waxed paper
CHAPTER 5	**What do animals eat for food?** p. 130	Matching Cards (Activity Master 2) safety scissors crayons or markers glue construction paper	
	How can you make a model of a food chain? pp. 154–155	crayons or markers masking tape	paper plates yarn
UNIT B	**How can color help mice stay hidden from hawks?** pp. 164–165	glue (optional)	navy bean seeds black-eyed pea bean seeds black bean seeds paper plate resealable clear plastic bags timer

Equipment Kit Includes:

▶ materials in chapter bags
▶ mobile storage box
▶ activity placemats and trays
▶ Teacher's Activity Guides

Bears

The grizzly bear is the state animal. Many years ago, about 5,000 of these bears lived in California. Some lived near the ocean. Some lived in the valleys. The bears ate nuts, fruit, insects, fish, plants, and small animals.

People did not like grizzlies. Grizzlies ate farm animals. People killed the grizzlies. This helped farmers.

Grizzly bears once lived in valleys. Valleys are large, low areas between mountains. There are rivers and streams in valleys. People moved into the valleys and cut down many trees. They planted food. The bears had no place to live. They went to the mountains but the mountains were not a good place for them. There were fewer and fewer bears.

The last one was killed in 1922. Now no grizzly bears live in California.

The black bear still lives in California. Black bears live in forests. They live in the mountains. They eat plants and very small animals.

Black bears like our food. They look for it near people. When people go camping, they must keep their food safe. Bears also like anything that is smelly. They will even eat garbage! Black bears also like beehives, fruit farms, and gardens.

Most black bears are scared of people. Black bears live far from farm land, so they do not bother the farmers.

The trees where the black bears lived were not all cut down. Black bears are used to living near people.

There were 6,000 black bears 25 years ago. Now there are more. About 30,000 black bears live in California.

Estimated Number of Bears in the State	
Year	**Number of Bears**
1983	6,000
1993	16,000
2003	30,000

Fun Facts

- ▶ A black bear can run 35 miles an hour.
- ▶ Adult black bears weigh 125 to 350 pounds.
- ▶ Female black bears have 2–4 cubs. They usually have cubs every two years.
- ▶ A wild black bear may live 25 years.
- ▶ In the U.S., there are about 325,000 black bears.
- ▶ The California grizzly bear was made the official state animal in 1953. It is on the state flag and the state seal.

Chapter 3
Needs of Plants and Animals

CALIFORNIA Standards Preview

1LS2.0 Plants and animals meet their needs in different ways. As a basis for understanding this concept:

1LS2.b Students know both plants and animals need water, animals need food, and plants need light.

1LS2.e Students know roots are associated with the intake of water and soil nutrients and green leaves are associated with making food from sunlight.

1IE4.0 Scientific progress is made by asking meaningful questions and conducting careful investigations. As a basis for understanding this concept and addressing the content in the other three strands, students should develop their own questions and perform investigations.

1IE4.b Record observations and data with pictures, numbers, or written statements.

Standards Focus Questions

- What do plants need?
- How do plants get what they need?
- What do animals need?

LESSON TITLES AND PACING

California Science CONTENT STANDARDS

Needs of Plants and Animals

Lab zone **Directed Inquiry**

Explore
Do plants need water?
p. 76

⏱ 15 min

1LS2.b Students know both plants and animals need water, animals need food, and plants need light.
1IE4.b Record observations and data with pictures, numbers, or written statements.

LESSON **1**

What do plants need?
pp. 78–81

⏱ 30 min

1LS2.b Students know both plants and animals need water, animals need food, and plants need light.

LESSON **2**

How do plants get what they need?
pp. 82–85

⏱ 30 min

1LS2.e Students know roots are associated with the intake of water and soil nutrients and green leaves are associated with making food from sunlight.

LESSON **3**

What do animals need?
pp. 86–87

⏱ 20 min

1LS2.b Students know both plants and animals need water, animals need food, and plants need light.

Lab zone **Guided Inquiry**

Investigate
Do plants need light?
pp. 90–91

⏱ 15 min

1LS2.b Students know both plants and animals need water, animals need food, and plants need light.
1LS2.e Students know roots are associated with the intake of water and soil nutrients and green leaves are associated with making food from sunlight.
1IE4.b Record observations and data with pictures, numbers, or written statements.

Reviewing Key Concepts

⏱ 25 min

Review and assess each science content standard from the chapter as listed above.

Chapter 3 Review/Test
pp. 92–95

VOCAB/SKILLS	ASSESSMENT/INTERVENTION
Process Skills: Observe Infer	• **Explain Your Results,** SE p. 76 • **Activity Recording Sheet,** *Science Study Notebook* p. 36 • **Activity Rubric,** *Science Study Notebook Teacher's Guide* p. T24
living	• **Scaffolded Questions,** TE pp. 79, 81 • **Chapter Study Guide,** *Science Study Notebook* pp. 31–32 • **Lesson Study Guide,** *Science Study Notebook* p. 38 • **Lesson Quiz,** *Assessment Book* p. 33
roots **nutrients** **leaves**	• **Scaffolded Questions,** TE pp. 83, 85 • **Lesson Study Guide,** *Science Study Notebook* p. 39 • **Lesson Quiz,** *Assessment Book* p. 34
	• **Scaffolded Questions,** TE p. 86 • **Lesson Study Guide,** *Science Study Notebook* p. 40 • **Lesson Quiz,** *Assessment Book* p. 35
Process Skills: Observe Predict	• **Explain Your Results,** SE p. 91 • **Activity Recording Sheet,** *Science Study Notebook* pp. 41–42 • **Activity Rubric,** *Science Study Notebook Teacher's Guide* p. T25
	• **Intervention and Reteaching Chart,** TE p. 95 • **Chapter Test,** *Assessment Book* pp. 37–40 • **Success Tracker** www.sfsuccessnet.com

DIGITAL CLASSROOM

Printable Resources
• *Science Study Notebook* pp. 31–42
• *Graphic Organizers,* TE pp. EMxxi, EMxxv
• *Intervention Study Guide* pp. 22–27
• *Assessment Book* pp. 31–40
• *Teacher's Activity Guide* pp. 16–17
• LabZone Activities

AudioText
Unit B, Chapter 3

eTools
Place-Value Blocks

Activity Videos
Unit B, Chapter 3

UNIVERSAL ACCESS

English Learners
TE pp. 79, 83, 87

Special Needs
TE pp. 80, 84, 87

Advanced Learners
TE pp. 80, 84, 87

Extra Support
TE pp. 81, 85, 87

CONTENT READERS

The *Science Content Readers Teacher's Guide* includes California Science Content Standards.

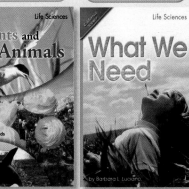

DIFFERENTIATED INSTRUCTION

Content Readers deliver the same standards, vocabulary, concepts, and skills as the chapter and can be used for original instruction, reteaching, and enrichment.

Below-Level

On-Level

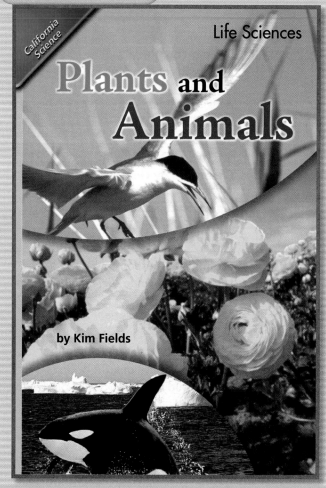

Summary

Living things can change and grow, and they have needs. Plants need air, light, water, and food. Roots hold plants in the ground and take in water and nutrients. Leaves use water, nutrients, air, and light to make food for the plant. Animals need air, water, and food to live.

Summary

Living things can grow and change. Plants are living things. They need certain things to stay alive and grow. Plants need sunlight, air, nutrients, and water. Most plants have the same parts. They have roots, which keep a plant in the ground. The stem takes water and nutrients to different parts of the plant. Leaves of green plants make their own food. Animals are also living things. Animals need air, water, and food to live.

CONTENT READER DATABASE SUPPORT

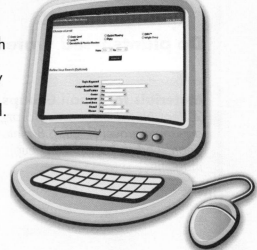

Use the online database to search for additional content readers by title, content, and target reading skill.

Above-Level

California Science

Life Sciences

What We Need

by Barbara L. Luciano

Summary

All living things can grow and change. Plants, animals, and people are living things. Living things have needs. Plants need air, water, light from the Sun, and space to grow. Animals need air, water, food, and space to live. Animals also need shelter. People need air, water, food, and shelter too.

Extended Vocabulary for Above-Level Content Reader

dens	lungs
dirty	soil
healthy	space

▶ To use the online database, go to **www.sfsuccessnet.com**, and enter your User ID and password from your Teacher Access Pack.

▶ Once logged in, enter the database.

▶ Choose a reading level or a range, or choose other search criteria.

▶ Specify content area, comprehension skill, and/or theme.

▶ Assign text, matching appropriate reading levels for children.

▶ Assign readers to individual children.

▶ Listen to each selection.

▶ Download and print.

▶ Print lesson plans and worksheets for each reader.

Lab zone Directed Inquiry

1LS2.b **Life Sciences** Students know both plants and animals need water, animals need food, and plants need light.

1IE4.b **Investigation and Experimentation** Record observations and data with pictures, numbers, or written statements.

Explore ⏱ 15 min
Do plants need water? p. 76

Materials for Small Groups
*2 clear plastic deli bowls (16 oz);
aquarium gravel ($\frac{1}{2}$ cup); 8 pinto
bean seeds;* water ($\frac{1}{4}$ to $\frac{1}{3}$ cup);
magnifier

Materials listed in *italics* are kit materials.

Advance Preparation Put $\frac{1}{4}$ cup of gravel and four seeds in each bowl. Add about $\frac{1}{4}$ cup of water to one of the bowls. The water should not cover the gravel.

Teaching Tips Ask children how the contents of the two bowls differ. Tell children to use a magnifier to observe the seeds in the bowls each day. Discuss with them what they observe. To make pictorial records, children should draw the contents of each bowl for four successive days. Within each of two overall drawings titled *Bowl with Water* and *Bowl Without Water*, children should create four individual pictures with the captions *Day 1, Day 2, Day 3,* and *Day 4*. Any observed changes in the seeds should be drawn and labeled. Have children use their drawings to describe how seeds need water to grow.

What to Expect The seeds in the bowl with water will sprout after three or four days.

 Activity Video
Unit B, Chapter 3

 Activity Placemat
Mat 6

Guided Inquiry

1LS2.b Life Sciences Students know both plants and animals need water, animals need food, and plants need light.

1LS2.e Life Sciences Students know roots are associated with the intake of water and soil nutrients and green leaves are associated with making food from sunlight.

1IE4.b Investigation and Experimentation Record observations and data with pictures, numbers, or written statements.

Investigate ⏱ 15 min
Do plants need light? pp. 90–91

Materials for Small Groups
2 clear plastic cups (9 oz); grass seeds (about 1 tsp); potting soil (about 1¼ c); water (about ¼ c); pouring container (for water); washable paints (optional)

Materials listed in *italics* are kit materials.

Alternative Materials
If children are planting their own seeds, you may want to use soil pellets. They are much easier to use and less messy.

Advance Preparation Plant seeds about ten days in advance. Cover seeds with a thin layer of soil. Keep soil moist. Prepare 2 cups per group.

Tips Be careful not to over-water the seeds. In simple words, explain to children that plants absorb sunlight, which helps them meet their energy requirements. Point out how the plant grows toward the light to improve its ability to make food in the green leaves of the plant.

What to Expect The plant placed in sunlight will grow. The plant placed in darkness will not grow and may turn brown.

 **Activity Video** Unit B, Chapter 3

 **Activity Placemat** Mat 7

Additional Activity Resources
The following resources are available for activities found in the Student Edition.

 Printable Resources

▶ *Science Study Notebook*
  • Activity Recording Sheets
    Recording sheets provide structure to help children record data from each activity.
  • Activity Rubrics
    Teachers can monitor children's own progress using the Activity Rubric in the *Science Study Notebook Teacher's Guide.*
▶ *Teacher's Activity Guide* For detailed information about Inquiry Activities, access the *Teacher's Activity Guide* at **www.sfsuccessnet.com**.

 Activity Videos
Prepare for and rehearse each activity before class by watching a video of the activity.

> *"As students progress through the three stages of inquiry, support from the teacher diminishes and student ownership increases."*
>
> —Dr. Karen Ostlund, UTeach, College of Natural Sciences, The University of Texas at Austin

SCIENCE STUDY NOTEBOOK SUPPORT
A companion to the Student Edition

Scott Foresman
Science Study Notebook
• Chapter Preview
• Lesson Study Guides
• Vocabulary Support
• How to Read Science Support
• Recording Sheets for All Activities

1
California
Science

▶ **Chapter Study Guide**
Children preview and organize the key concepts in the chapter.

▶ **Chapter Vocabulary Cards** Children cut out cards to use with suggested strategies in the Teacher's Edition.

▶ **Chapter Vocabulary Preview** Children are introduced to science words.

▶ **How to Read Science** Children record answers for the Student Edition page.

▶ **Lesson Study Guides** Children practice note-taking as they learn key concepts while reading.

▶ **Inquiry Activities** *Science Study Notebook Teacher's Guide* provides an Activity Rubric to evaluate children's progress.

▶ **Printable Resources** All pages of the *Science Study Notebook* are available to purchasers of Scott Foresman California Science ©2008 at **www.sfsuccessnet.com**.

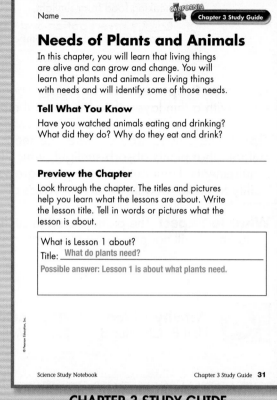

CHAPTER 3 STUDY GUIDE
Science Study Notebook, p. 31

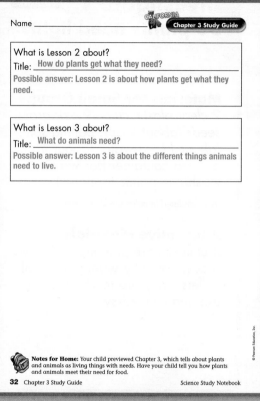

CHAPTER 3 STUDY GUIDE
Science Study Notebook, p. 32

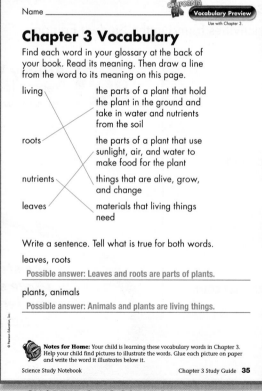

CHAPTER 3 VOCABULARY PREVIEW
Science Study Notebook, p. 35

LESSON 1 STUDY GUIDE
Science Study Notebook, p. 38

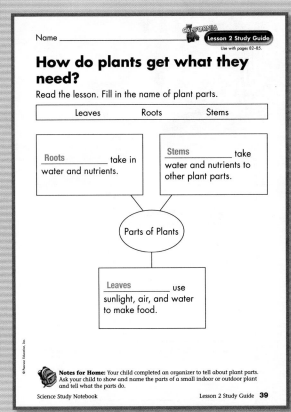

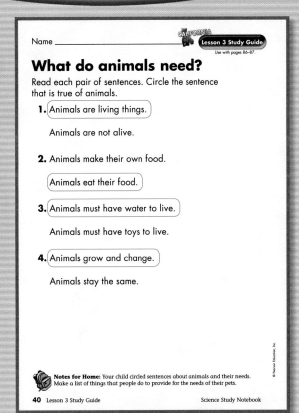

LESSON 2 STUDY GUIDE
Science Study Notebook, p. 39

LESSON 3 STUDY GUIDE
Science Study Notebook, p. 40

Scott Foresman
Assessment Book
- Chapter Pretests
- Lesson Quizzes
- Chapter and Unit Tests
- Summative Test

California Science

Printable Resources All pages of the *Assessment Book* are available to purchasers of Scott Foresman California Science ©2008 at **www.sfsuccessnet.com**.

CHAPTER 3 PRETEST
Assessment Book, p. 31

Name _____
Chapter 3 Pretest

Read each question and choose the best answer. Then fill in the circle next to the correct answer.

1. Which part helps an animal move through water?
   - Ⓐ fin
   - Ⓑ shell
   - Ⓒ wing
   - Ⓓ claw

2. What part holds up a plant?
   - Ⓐ root
   - Ⓑ leaf
   - Ⓒ stem
   - Ⓓ seed

3. Which thing comes first?
   - Ⓐ   Ⓑ   Ⓒ   Ⓓ

Assessment Book   Chapter 3 Pretest **31**

CHAPTER 3 PRETEST
Assessment Book, p. 32

Name _____
Chapter 3 Pretest

4. Which of these is a living thing?
   - Ⓐ the sun
   - Ⓑ a dog
   - Ⓒ a rock
   - Ⓓ the moon

5. Which picture shows a liquid?

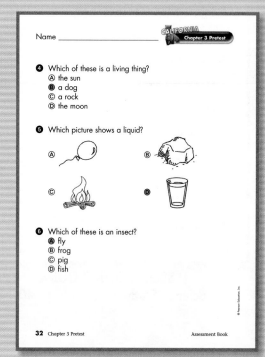

   - Ⓐ   Ⓑ
   - Ⓒ   Ⓓ

6. Which of these is an insect?
   - Ⓐ fly
   - Ⓑ frog
   - Ⓒ pig
   - Ⓓ fish

32 Chapter 3 Pretest   Assessment Book

LESSON 1 QUIZ
Assessment Book, p. 33

Name _____
Lesson 1 Quiz
Use with pages 79–81.

Complete the Sentence
Write the word that completes each sentence.

| grow | living | needs | Sun |

1. All living things have ___needs___.

2. Plants can ___grow___ and change.

3. Plants get light from the ___Sun___.

4. Plants are ___living___ things.

Apply What You Learned
5. You are caring for a friend's plant. What must you do to keep the plant healthy?
   I must make sure that the plant has air, water, and sunlight.

Assessment Book   Lesson 1 Quiz **33**

LESSON 2 QUIZ
Assessment Book, p. 34

Name _____
Lesson 2 Quiz
Use with pages 82–85.

Complete the Sentence
Write the word that completes each sentence.

| ground | leaves | nutrients | roots |

1. The ___roots___ of a plant take in water from the soil.

2. Materials that living things need are called ___nutrients___.

3. Food is made in the ___leaves___ of a green plant.

4. The roots of a plant hold the plant in the ___ground___.

Apply What You Learned
5. What do green plants need to make food?
   Green plants need sunlight, air, and water to make food.

34 Lesson 2 Quiz   Assessment Book

LESSON 3 QUIZ
Assessment Book, p. 35

Name _____
Lesson 3 Quiz
Use with pages 86–87.

Complete the Sentence
Write the word that completes each sentence.

| air | change | food | living |

1. Animals are ___living___ things.

2. Animals eat ___food___ to live.

3. Animals need ___air___ and water.

4. Animals grow and ___change___.

Apply What You Learned
5. Tell why a rock is not a living thing.
   A rock does not grow and change.

Assessment Book   Lesson 3 Quiz **35**

Entry-Level Assessment	Progress-Monitoring Assessment	Summative Assessment
► **Assessment Book:** Chapter 3 Pretest	**Ongoing Assessment** ► **Student Edition:** Checkpoint and Lesson Review questions ► **Teacher's Edition:** Diagnostic Check and Scaffolded Questions ► **Assessment Book:** Lesson Quizzes	► **Student Edition:** Unit B California Standards Practice ► **Assessment Book:** Chapter 3 Test Unit B Test Summative Test
	DIGITAL **Success Tracker** Chapter 3 online assessment and reteaching **Formal Assessment** ► **Student Edition:** Chapter 3 Review/Test ► DIGITAL **ExamView** Customizable Chapter 3 Test	

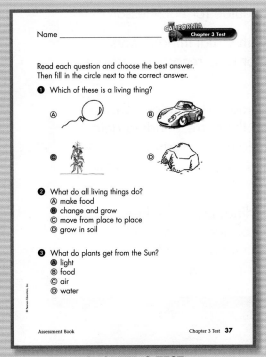

CHAPTER 3 TEST
Assessment Book, p. 37

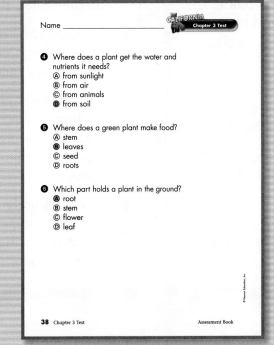

CHAPTER 3 TEST
Assessment Book, p. 38

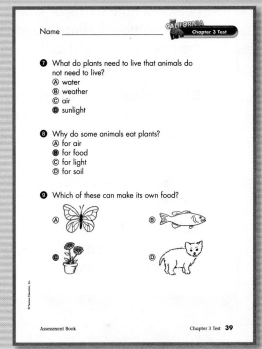

CHAPTER 3 TEST
Assessment Book, p. 39

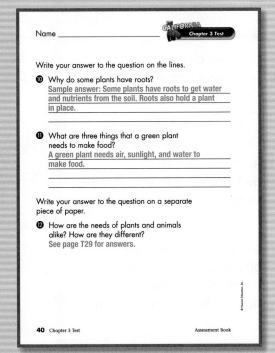

CHAPTER 3 TEST
Assessment Book, p. 40

Strategies

Use these suggested strategies to help you customize instruction for children with individual needs.

Strategies for
English Learners

Word Collection Books

▶ Have children enter words into word collection books. Words may be collected on personal note cards or entered in a binder or spiral notebook. Encourage children to use their personal word collections for ongoing study or reference.

▶ **Beginning** Ask children to write a word on one side of a card or page and draw a picture to illustrate its meaning on the back.

▶ **Intermediate** Tell children to write a word on one side and draw and define it on the back.

▶ **Advanced** Have children write a word on one side and draw, define, and use it in a sentence on the back.

Strategies for
Special Needs

Using a Study Guide

▶ Help children develop an understanding of the chapter's main idea and details by providing an annotated study guide for each lesson.

▶ To assist children with visual impairments, provide large print or tape recorded versions of the study guide.

▶ Review the study guide with children. Discuss each main idea and the corresponding details, and help children relate the information to real-world examples of what plants and animals need.

▶ To assess understanding, have children develop a summary of each lesson. Tell children that their summaries can be tape recorded, written, or pictorial.

Strategies for
Advanced Learners

Learning Centers

▶ Review the chapter essential question with children. Have children identify and define the vocabulary terms.

▶ Organize children into three groups. Assign each group one of the lesson focus questions: *What do plants need? How do plants get what they need? What do animals need?*

▶ Have each group develop a learning center that addresses its particular question.

▶ Encourage children to include a variety of elements in their centers, such as games, experiments, and question/answer activities. Remind children to include answers so that other children can self-check their work.

Strategies for
Extra Support

I Predict

▶ Have children examine the chapter's illustrations, captions, lesson focus questions, headings, and boldface vocabulary terms before reading the chapter.

▶ Based on this overview, have children use a graphic organizer such as the one on TE p. EMxxii to predict answers to the chapter essential question: *What do plants and animals need?*

▶ As children read the chapter, have them check their predictions and provide oral summary statements indicating how closely their predictions matched the information in the student text.

Integrated Universal Access

	English Learners	Special Needs	Advanced Learners	Extra Support
1LS2.b Students know both plants and animals need water, animals need food, and plants need light.	**Caring for Plants** TE p. 79	**Make a Schedule** TE p. 80	**Ecology** TE p. 80	**Observe Living and Nonliving Flowers** TE p. 81
	Needs of Plants and Animals TE p. 87	**Observe and Care for a Class Pet** TE p. 87	**Animal Needs Book** TE p. 87	**Animal Needs Mobile** TE p. 87
1LS2.e Students know roots are associated with the intake of water and soil nutrients and green leaves are associated with making food from sunlight.	**Plants and the Environment** TE p. 83	**Examine Plant Parts** TE p. 84	**Dramatize Plants Making Food** TE p. 84	**Put Things in Order** TE p. 85

California English-Language Arts
CONTENT STANDARDS FOCUS

1RW1.0 Word Analysis, Fluency, and Systematic Vocabulary Development Students understand the basic features of reading. They select letter patterns and know how to translate them into spoken language by using phonics, syllabication, and word parts. They apply this knowledge to achieve fluent oral and silent reading.

Objective Students determine meaning and increase vocabulary as they read science.

Focus on the **Big Idea** 🕐 20 min

Chapter 3 Vocabulary Terms

living, p. 79   nutrients, p. 83
roots, p. 83   leaves, p. 84

🖨 **Printable Pretest** Assess children's background knowledge with Chapter 3 Pretest on *Assessment Book* pp. 31–32.

1. Build Background

Warm Up
Activate Prior Knowledge

▸ Ask children the essential question, *What do plants and animals need?* Save responses for later in the chapter.

▸ Ask children to tell what they know about caring for plants and animals. Invite them to share some experiences they have had with pets and plants in their homes. On the board, list some of the things they did to care for plants and animals.

2. Introduce Vocabulary

Preview Terms
🖨 **Printable Graphic Organizer** Use *Graphic Organizer 7* (TE p. EMxxv) to focus children's attention on science vocabulary as they read Chapter 3.

▸ Many science vocabulary words are abstract. Use the pictures and labels on these pages to help you open a discussion about science concepts and build academic language.

▸ List the vocabulary terms on the board. Have children pronounce each word as you write it. Discuss the meaning of each word and how it relates to the needs of plants and animals.

Focus on the BIG Idea

What do plants and animals need?

roots   nutrients

74 DIGITAL 9

Big Idea

Both plants and animals need water and air. Animals need food. Plants need light to make food.

Teacher Background

▸ In addition to needing water and air, both plants and animals need a source of energy to survive. Plants absorb sunlight and animals eat food to meet their energy requirements.

▸ While it is true that all animals need food, individual species gather and eat their food in a wide variety of ways.

living

leaves

75

Share and Talk

Use questions such as the following to help children clarify their understanding of the vocabulary words.

▶ How are the words *roots* and *nutrients* related? Roots take in nutrients from the soil.

▶ Which things shown on pp. 74–75 are living? The plants, trees, and deer are living.

Science Study Notebook

Printable Resources

Chapter Vocabulary Preview

To give children practice using academic language, have them complete the chapter vocabulary preview on p. 35.

Vocabulary Cards Have children use the vocabulary cards on pp. 33–34 to draw a picture. Children should choose two vocabulary cards and draw a picture of each vocabulary term.

3. Practice

Active Glossary Reinforce science vocabulary and concepts with Active Glossary animations.

Vocabulary Strategy

Grouping Terms Tell children that they can sort like words together. Give an example by stating that the words *wheel*, *tire*, and *seat* go together because they are all parts of cars.

Ask: Which words on pp. 74–75 go together? The words *roots* and *leaves* go together because they are both parts of plants.

1LS2.b **Life Sciences** Students know both plants and animals need water, animals need food, and plants need light.

1IE4.b **Investigation and Experimentation** Record observations and data with pictures, numbers, or written statements.

Objective Students describe how seeds and plants need water to grow.

Directed Inquiry

⏱ 15 min

1. Get Ready

Materials for Small Groups

2 clear plastic bowls   water
aquarium gravel   *magnifier*
8 pinto bean seeds

Materials listed in *italics* are kit materials.

2. What to Do

Preview

▶ Conduct an inventory of materials with children. For English Learners, solicit alternative names for items in their home language. Post the names of materials and other academic language, such as *seeds, plants, data,* and *observe,* on a word wall.

▶ You may wish to preview science content in Lesson 1.

Advance Preparation Put $\frac{1}{4}$ cup of gravel and four seeds in each bowl. Add about $\frac{1}{4}$ cup of water to one of the bowls. The water should not cover the gravel.

Tips

▶ Ask children how the contents of the two bowls differ.

▶ Tell children to use a magnifier to observe the seeds in the bowls each day. Discuss what they observe.

▶ Have children use their drawings to describe how seeds need water to grow.

3. Explain Your Results

Science Study Notebook

Printable Resources Activity Recording Sheet
Discuss the results by reviewing completed p. 36. Ask volunteers to explain how plants and seeds need water.

Activity Rubric Use *Science Study Notebook Teacher's Guide* p. T24 to evaluate children's work.

 Directed Inquiry

Explore Do plants need water?

Materials

bowl with gravel

bowl with gravel and water

bean seeds

magnifier

What to Do

① Put 4 bean seeds on the gravel in each bowl.

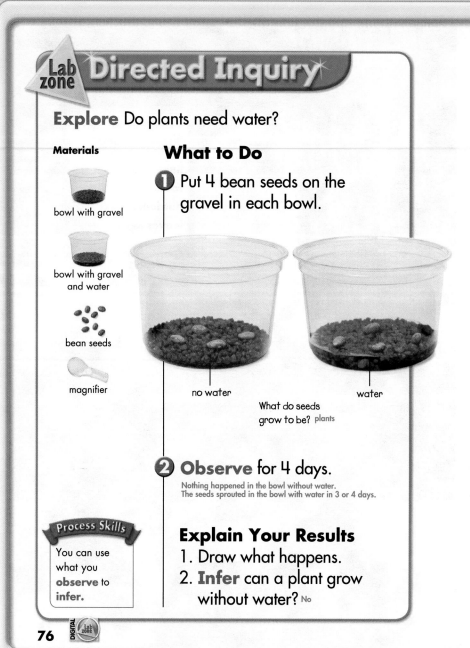

no water   water

What do seeds grow to be? plants

② **Observe** for 4 days.
Nothing happened in the bowl without water. The seeds sprouted in the bowl with water in 3 or 4 days.

Process Skills

You can use what you **observe** to **infer.**

Explain Your Results

1. Draw what happens.
2. **Infer** can a plant grow without water? No

76

Digital Classroom

Activity Video Prepare for and rehearse the activity before class.

Printable Activity Rubric Monitor children's progress using the Activity Rubric located at **www.sfsuccessnet.com**.

Printable LabZone Activity Provide children with additional activities located at **www.sfsuccessnet.com**.

Call **1-888-537-4908** with activity questions.

Big Idea	Teacher Background
A seed needs water to grow.	▶ Inside every seed is the dormant embryo of the plant that will grow out of it under the right environmental conditions. ▶ Water is absorbed into the seed, where it begins chemical processes that create sugars, which provide energy for the embryo.

How to Read Science

Reading Skills

Relate Prior Knowledge

Relate prior knowledge means to use what you know already about a topic.

Science Story

Grassland

These animals live in a grassland. Animals need food and water to live. They need food and water to grow and change.

Apply It!

Infer Look at the picture. Why do you think the animals have come to the water hole?

Tell what I Know.

77

English-Language Arts Support

1RC2.6 Reading Comprehension

▶ **Printable Graphic Organizer** Use *Graphic Organizer 3* (TE p. EMxxi) with children to help them record what they already know about a topic.

▶ To help meet the needs of children whose reading skills are below grade level, help them use their prior knowledge to break down the term *grassland*. Ask them what two words they hear in *grassland*, and have them tell what each word means. Ask: *Based on these two words, what do you think a grassland is like?* Encourage children to tell what they think a grassland is like based on these two words.

California English-Language Arts
CONTENT STANDARDS FOCUS

1RC2.6 Reading Comprehension Relate prior knowledge to textual information.

Objective Students use their prior knowledge to help comprehend a science story.

How to Read Science 25 min

1. Build Background

Comprehension Skill: Relate Prior Knowledge

Tell children that they can use what they already know to better understand what they read.

Ask: Think about a pet animal you or a friend have. What does the animal need to live? Possible answer: It needs food, water, air, and shelter.

2. Teach

Grassland

Read the science story with children. Point out to children that animals living in a grassland have the same basic needs as animals living in other places.

Science Study Notebook

Printable Recording Sheet To help children understand how to relate prior knowledge, have them complete the How to Read Science recording sheet on p. 37.

3. Summarize and Assess

Apply It!

Relating prior knowledge means to take what you already know and use it to better understand what you read. Work with children to complete the graphic organizer using information from the science story "Grassland."

Tell what I know.

Possible answer: Animals need water to live. The animals have come to drink water.

Life Sciences Students know both plants and animals need water, animals need food, and plants need light.

Objective Students tell what plants need to survive.

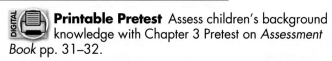 **Chapter 3 Lesson 1** ◐ **30 min**

What do plants need?

1. Build Background

Printable Pretest Assess children's background knowledge with Chapter 3 Pretest on *Assessment Book* pp. 31–32.

Science Song Listen to the song "Living Things." Look at the picture. Have children identify some living things in the picture. Then ask children whether there are things in the picture that are not alive (dirt, rocks, air). Explain that things that are not alive are referred to as *nonliving*. Discuss what children think they might learn about living things in this chapter.

Standards Warm Up

Activate Prior Knowledge Show children a potted plant and ask them if they have plants at home. Talk about their plants and ask children what they do to take care of the plants.

2. Teach

⋙ QUICK Plan

▶ As a class, take a picture walk through the lesson to discuss visuals and captions.

▶ **AudioText** Use the audio version of the Student Edition at a technology center.

▶ Encourage children to work in teams to answer lesson questions.

Science Study Notebook

Printable Chapter Study Guide
Have children check their understanding of Chapter 3 by completing pp. 31–32 as they read.

You Are There

Living Things

Sung to the tune of "Found a Peanut"
Lyrics by Gerri Brioso & Richard Freitas/The Dovetail Group, Inc.

Plants are living things. So are animals.
So are people, yes we know.
Living things need food and water.
Living things all change and grow.

78

Big Idea	Teacher Background
Plants need air, water, and sunlight to live.	▶ Plants can live in almost any environment where there is air, water, and sunlight. However, different plants have different needs.
	▶ Some plants, such as cacti, yuccas, and sagebrush, are able to live in deserts. These plants need very little water to survive. They are also able to withstand harsh direct sunlight.
	▶ Other plants, such as ferns and vines, survive in the understory (middle layer) of tropical forests, where much of the sunlight is blocked out by taller trees. These plants thrive on a large amount of moisture.

Lesson 1

What do plants need?

Living things are alive.
Plants are living things.
Plants can grow and change.
Living things have needs.

This deer is a living thing too. **2**

79

▶ Read p. 79 with children. Then read the title of the lesson again. Ask children to predict what plants need to live.

▶ Help children to confirm their predictions by identifying key words when they read the lesson.

Scaffolded Questions

Use the following guiding questions to monitor children's comprehension.

1 **Define** What is a living thing? A living thing is something that is alive.

2 **Identify** What is one living thing on pp. 78–79? Possible answers: A deer, a tree, a plant

3 **Contrast** What if something is not alive and does not grow and change? It is not a living thing.

Extend Science Vocabulary

▶ Tell children that the root of the word **living** is *live*.

▶ Have children name other words that have *live* as a root, such as *alive, lives, lively,* and *lived*. List the words on the board.

▶ Discuss the meanings of these words and how they are similar and different.

▶ **9** **Active Glossary** Children who need more practice with vocabulary terms may review vocabulary online or use vocabulary cards (*Science Study Notebook,* pp. 33–34).

Universal Access

English Learners
Caring for Plants Bring in a grown plant and review with children the text on p. 80 about what plants need to live. Write the words *air, water,* and *sunlight* on the board. Say each word and show children how to provide each need to the grown plant.

LSB3 **ELD Listening and Speaking**
Beginning Ask children, "What do plants need?" Point to the words and have children repeat them. Ask volunteers to choose one of the words written on the board and show how to care for the plant by providing that need.

REI8 **ELD Reading**
Intermediate Have children make a picture book showing each need of a plant. Ask them to draw three pictures and to label them using the words on the board. Allow children to share their books.

WA4 **ELD Writing**
Advanced Have children write three sentences telling what plants need to live. Allow children to begin their sentences using: *Plants need _____ .* Encourage children to read their sentences to a partner.

Diagnostic Check

If . . . after hearing the song on p. 78, children have difficulty understanding how plants and animals are living things,

then . . . help them find and cut out pictures of each from magazines. Use the pictures to make two class posters, labeled *Plants* and *Animals.* You may also extend this activity by having children find pictures of nonliving things and providing an opportunity to compare and contrast living and nonliving things.

Science Study Notebook

 Printable Lesson Study Guide
Have children check their understanding of Lesson 1 by completing p. 38 as they read.

Share and Talk

Have children care for a growing plant. Ask each child to plant a bean seed in a plastic cup partially filled with soil. To help facilitate growth, soak the seeds overnight before planting them. Discuss with children the needs of plants and how to care for them. Allow children to determine where to put their plant to get the sunlight it needs to make its own food. Have children water their plant on a regular basis. Observe the growth of the plants and take or draw pictures of them to record their progress.

Ask: What are some ways that plants get water? From the rain; from a person watering them

Write About Science

1WA2.1 **Writing Applications** Ask children to write a brief narrative describing how to take care of the plant.

Writing Rubric

4	The child's writing is clear and focused. The narrative provides many details describing how to care for all the plant's needs.
3	The child's writing is focused. The narrative provides some details describing how to care for the plant's needs.
2	The child's writing is somewhat focused. The narrative shows a limited understanding of the plant's needs. Sentences have many mistakes.
1	The child's writing reveals a limited understanding of the plant's needs or how to care for the plant. Words are written, but there are no sentences.

Tip

Help children begin their narratives by writing these statements on the board: "Mrs. Rader gave me a plant. I am going to take care of it by . . ."

What Plants Need

① A need is something a living thing must have to live.
Plants need air to live.
Plants need water.

Plants need light too.
Plants get light from the Sun.
② Plants need light to grow and change.

Rain can give plants the water they need.

③

80

Universal Access

Special Needs

Make a Schedule Help children make a schedule to ensure that their plant is watered on a regular basis. Include the amount of water to use and how often the plant needs to be watered. Set a specific time of the day for children to water and check their plant.

Advanced Learners

Ecology After children have had the experience of planting and growing a bean plant, write the word *ecology* on the board. Explain that *ecology* refers to how plants and animals depend upon each other and upon the places where they live. Have children work in groups or as a class to make a poster about ecology. Write the word *Plants* in the center. To the left of *Plants*, have children write things that plants need. To the right of *Plants*, have children write things that need plants.

The Sun gives these flowers the light they need to grow.

Lesson Review 1. Plants need air, water, and light.

1. What do plants need to live?

TARGET SKILL 2. **Relate Prior Knowledge** Tell what might happen if a plant does not get light. 2. Possible answer: The plant might die.

81

Universal Access

Extra Support
Observe Living and Nonliving Flowers Have children compare and contrast a live potted plant with an artificial plant. Have children touch, smell, and observe the two and discuss the similarities and differences. Ask children what they would need to do to take care of each plant. Ask how each plant will change over time.

Scaffolded Questions

Use the following guiding questions to monitor children's comprehension.

1 **Define** What is a need? A need is something a living thing must have to live.

2 **Interpret** Why does a plant need light from the Sun? Possible answer: A plant needs light so it can grow and change.

3 **Decide** Do all plants need the same amount of water? How do you know? Possible answer: No. Some plants, such as cacti, can survive with little water for long periods of time.

Extend Science Vocabulary

▶ Discuss the difference between wants and needs. Tell children that a want may be something they long or hope for, but a need is something they must have to live.

▶ Help children identify wants and needs in their own lives. Ask them what they need to live. Write children's answers on the board. Answers might include food, water, shelter, and clothing.

▶ Point out that many things we say we need are really things we want. They are not things that we need to stay alive. Revisit the list of children's answers. For each answer, ask children, "Do you need this to live?"

3. Summarize and Assess

⯈ *QUICK* Summary

▶ Living things are alive.

▶ Living things have needs.

▶ Plants are living things.

▶ Plants need air, water, and sunlight to live and grow.

Assess

Printable Resources

Lesson Quiz Check for understanding by reviewing children's responses to *Assessment Book* p. 33 or to the Lesson Review in the Student Edition.

Intervention Study Guide Use pp. 22–23 to review and reinforce lesson concepts as needed.

1LS2.e **Life Sciences** Students know roots are associated with the intake of water and soil nutrients and green leaves are associated with making food from sunlight.

Objectives

▶ Students tell what nutrients are and explain the function of the roots of a plant.

▶ Students explain the function of plant leaves in making food.

Chapter 3   Lesson 2   30 min

How do plants get what they need?

1. Build Background

Standards Warm Up

Activate Prior Knowledge Ask children to observe and name different parts of the plants pictured on pp. 82–83. Help children identify flowers, stems, leaves, and roots. Explain to children that they will learn how some of these parts help a plant get what it needs to live and grow.

2. Teach

⇗ *QUICK* Plan

▶ As a class, take a picture walk through the lesson to discuss visuals and captions.

▶ **AudioText** Use the audio version of the Student Edition at a technology center.

▶ Encourage children to work in teams to answer lesson questions.

Science Study Notebook

Printable Lesson Study Guide
Have children check their understanding of Lesson 2 by completing p. 39 as they read.

Lesson 2

How do plants get what they need?

Many plants have the same parts.
These parts help a plant get what it needs.
These parts help a plant live and grow.

These plants have parts.

82

Big Idea	**Teacher Background**
Plants make their own food through a process called photosynthesis.	▶ Photosynthesis takes place in the green leaves of plants. Plant cells contain chloroplasts, which are filled with chlorophyll. Chlorophyll absorbs light energy from the Sun. This absorbed energy is used to turn water and carbon dioxide into sugars that the plant uses as food.
	Common Misconception Children might think that plants get food from the ground or from water. "Plant food" that is sold to gardeners is not food for plants. Plant food is usually placed in the soil to replace some nutrients, such as minerals and elements, that may be depleted. Plant food helps plants to grow and remain healthy.

Roots

Most plants have roots.

Roots hold a plant in the ground. ①

Roots take in water from the soil. ②

Roots take in nutrients from the soil.

Nutrients are materials that living things need. ③

1. ✓**Checkpoint** What are nutrients?
   1. Nutrients are materials that living things need.

2. **Relate Prior Knowledge** Tell how the roots help a plant get what it needs to live.
   2. Roots take in nutrients and water that plants need to live.

keyword: **roots** code: gr1p83

83

Universal Access

English Learners
Plants and the Environment Use a word web to review what plants need to live (air, water, and sunlight). Point to the pictures of roots and leaves on pp. 82–85 and explain how each part takes in the plant's needs. (For example, the roots take in water.)

RB4 **ELD Reading**
Beginning Have children draw a picture of a plant in an environment. Encourage them to include each of the things a plant needs. Help children to label the roots and leaves.

WE13 **ELD Writing**
Intermediate Have children draw a picture of a plant with roots and leaves, in an environment with air, water, and sunlight. Then have children copy and complete these sentences: The _____ take in water. The _____ take in energy from sunlight.

RA6 **ELD Reading**
Advanced Reread pp. 82–85. Ask children what they did to care for a plant (gave it air, water, and sunlight). Have children work with a partner to tell what the roots and leaves do for a plant.

Mathematics Support
1MG2.4 **Measurement and Geometry**

Point to a plant or part of a plant on pp. 82–83 and describe its position in relation to another plant or part using proximity, position, or direction words. Demonstrate with a sentence such as "The plant with the white flowers is to the *left of* the plant with no flowers." Have volunteers suggest their own sentences. Then ask children to describe the position of an object in two ways, such as "The white flower is *below* and to the *left of* the plant with roots."

Scaffolded Questions

Use the following guiding questions to monitor children's comprehension.

① **Name** What part of a plant holds it in the ground? Roots hold a plant in the ground.

② **Explain** How does a plant get water? The roots of a plant take in water from the soil.

③ **Conclude** Why is it important that plants take in nutrients? Plants need nutrients to live.

Extend Science Vocabulary

▶ Tell children that the **nutrients** found in the soil help plants live and grow. Remind children that all living things need nutrients.

▶ Ask children how they get nutrients (from food). Show children how nutrients such as folic acid, vitamins, and carbohydrates are listed on food boxes or cartons. Explain that these nutrients help their bodies to grow and change.

▶ **Active Glossary** Children who need more practice with vocabulary terms may review vocabulary online or use vocabulary cards (*Science Study Notebook,* pp. 33–34).

▶ **SciLinks** Children can go online to discover more about **roots** by using the NSTA *SciLink* available at **www.sfsuccessnet.com** (keyword: **roots** code: **gr1p83**).

Diagnostic Check

If . . . children have a difficult time conceptualizing how roots hold plants in the ground,

then . . . remind children that roots hold their teeth in their mouth. When a permanent tooth comes in, the roots of a baby tooth dissolve, which causes the tooth to fall out.

Share and Talk

Explain to children that the plant on pp. 84–85 has leaves that make food for the plant. Have children identify the parts of the plant. Discuss the function of each part in the making of food. Encourage children to identify the parts of other plants growing in the classroom.

Ask: What might happen to a plant if its stem broke? Some parts of the plant would not get the nutrients and water needed to make food. The plant would die.

Active Art Children can explore an interactive version of the plant on pp. 84–85 by using Active Art at **www.sfsuccessnet.com**.

Write About Science

1WS1.1 Writing Strategies Have children write sentences describing the function of the leaves and roots of a plant.

Writing Rubric

4	The child's writing is exceptionally clear and focused. It accurately describes the function of the plant parts. There are few or no mistakes.
3	The child's writing is clear and focused. It describes the function of the plant parts. There are some mistakes.
2	The child's writing is difficult to follow. It identifies the plant parts but provides an incomplete description of their function. There are many mistakes.
1	The child's writing identifies the plant parts but reveals a limited understanding of their function. There are many mistakes that make the writing difficult to understand.

Tips

To help children organize their ideas, make a chart listing the functions of the roots and leaves of a plant. Encourage children to look at the pictures on pp. 83–85 for visual support while writing.

Plants Make Food

Plants make their own food.
1 Leaves of green plants make food.
You might wonder how.

The stem takes water and nutrients from the roots.
The stem carries water and
2 nutrients to the leaves.

Roots

Stem

Leaves

Look for Active Art animations at www.sfsuccessnet.com

84

Universal Access

Special Needs

Examine Plant Parts Help reinforce children's understanding of the various parts of a plant by bringing a plant to class for children to examine. Allow children with visual impairments to touch the uprooted plant and help them to identify the leaf, flower, root, and stem. Discuss how each part helps the plant live. Encourage children to observe the firmness of the stem and length and fineness of the roots.

Advanced Learners

Dramatize Plants Making Food Have a group of children dramatize the functions of the parts of a plant. Encourage children to identify what plant part they represent and to tell how that part helps a plant get what it needs to grow. Allow children to make props, programs, and costumes for their performance.

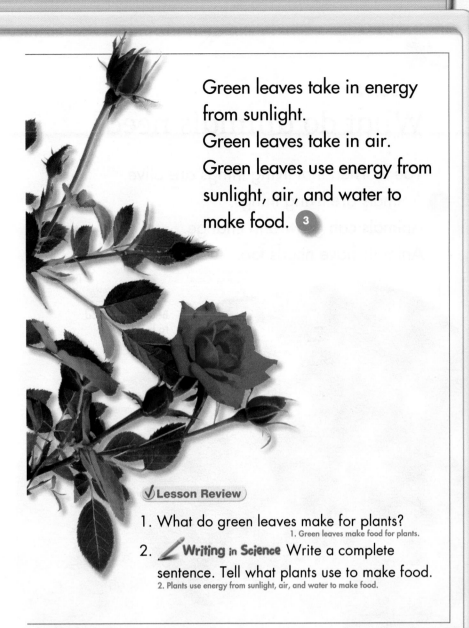

Green leaves take in energy from sunlight.

Green leaves take in air.

Green leaves use energy from sunlight, air, and water to make food.

✓ **Lesson Review**

1. What do green leaves make for plants?
   1. Green leaves make food for plants.

2. ✎ **Writing in Science** Write a complete sentence. Tell what plants use to make food.
   2. Plants use energy from sunlight, air, and water to make food.

85

Universal Access

Extra Support
Put Things in Order Have children create three drawings that show what the parts of a plant do—roots take in water and nutrients; stems carry water and nutrients to the leaves; green leaves use energy from sunlight, air, and water to make food. Have children mix up the drawings and then put them in order. Encourage children to describe each drawing.

Use the following guiding questions to monitor children's comprehension.

1 **Define** Which parts of plants make food? Leaves of plants make food.

2 **Explain** How do water and nutrients get from the roots to the leaves of a plant? The stem carries water and nutrients from the roots to the leaves.

3 **Predict** What might happen to a green plant that does not get any sunlight? The plant would not be able to make its own food, so it would die.

Extend Science Vocabulary

▶ Remind children that **leaves** is the plural form of *leaf*. Review what *plural* means (more than one).

▶ Explain that some words form the plural in this way, by changing the *f* to *v* and adding *-es*. Pronounce *leaf* and *leaves* so children can hear the difference.

▶ Then ask, "Can you think of other words that form the plural in the same way *leaf* does?" (Calf/calves; hoof/hooves; elf/elves)

▶ **DIGITAL 9** **Active Glossary** Children who need more practice with vocabulary terms may review vocabulary online or use vocabulary cards (*Science Study Notebook*, pp. 33–34).

3. Summarize and Assess

⬇ *QUICK* Summary

▶ The roots and leaves of a plant help it get what it needs to live and grow.

▶ Roots hold the plant in the ground and take in water and nutrients from the soil.

▶ Living things, such as plants, need nutrients.

▶ Green leaves use water, energy from sunlight, and air to make food for the plant.

Assess
DIGITAL 🖨 Printable Resources

Lesson Quiz Check for understanding by reviewing children's responses to *Assessment Book* p. 34 or to the Lesson Review in the Student Edition.

Intervention Study Guide Use pp. 24–25 to review and reinforce lesson concepts as needed.

1LS2.b **Life Sciences** Students know both plants and animals need water, animals need food, and plants need light.

Objective Students tell what animals need to survive.

Chapter 3 Lesson 3 ⏱ 20 min

What do animals need?

1. Build Background

Standards Warm Up
Activate Prior Knowledge Have children identify pets they have. Ask children to discuss the things their pets need (food, water, a clean cage or tank, exercise).

2. Teach

Science Study Notebook

Printable Lesson Study Guide
Have children check their understanding of Lesson 3 by completing p. 40 as they read.

Share and Talk
Have children discuss what the bears on pp. 86–87 need to live. Explain that animals get the energy they need to grow and change from the food they eat.

Ask: What would you do to take care of a pet's needs? Answers will vary but should include feeding and giving water to the pet.

Scaffolded Questions

Use the following guiding questions to monitor children's comprehension.

1 **Recall** What kinds of things are both plants and animals? Plants and animals are living things.

2 **Apply** What does a bear need to live? A bear needs food, air, and water to live.

3 **Compare** How is the way animals get energy different from the way plants get energy? Animals get energy from food. Plants take in energy from sunlight.

Lesson 3

What do animals need?

You learned that living things are alive.
1 Animals are living things.
Animals can grow and change.
Animals have needs too.

Munch!
Bears need food to live.

86

Big Ideas	Teacher Background
Living things need energy.	▶ All living things need energy. Plants use the energy from sunlight to create their own food. Animals get energy from the food they eat.
Learning what plants and animals need to survive is one of the foundations of ecology.	▶ The science of ecology studies the relationship of living things to their environment and to each other.
	▶ Plants and animals depend on the air, soil, water, and sunlight in an environment to live. They are adapted to specific conditions of these resources in their environment—the quality of air, type of soil, amount of water and sunlight, ranges in temperature. If these conditions change in their environment, plants and animals may not be able to survive.

Animals need air to live.
Animals need water to live.
Animals need food too.
Animals get energy from food.

 **Lesson Review**

1. What do animals need to live?
   1. Animals need air, water, and food to live.

2. Tell why a bear is a living thing.
   2. Possible answer: A bear is a living thing because it has needs and can grow and change.

Slurp!

Bears need
water to live.

87

▶ Write the word *food* on the board.

▶ Ask children to name some of their favorite foods.

▶ Ask children if they think wood is a type of food. Explain that a termite is a kind of animal that eats wood. Wood is food for a termite.

▶ Ask children to think about what they learned about sunlight and the leaves of plants. Remind children that plants use energy from sunlight to make their own food.

▶ Explain that food gives animals the energy they need to live and grow.

3. Summarize and Assess

⟫ *QUICK* Summary

▶ Animals are living things and can grow and change.

▶ Animals need air, water, and food to live.

Assess
Printable Resources

Lesson Quiz Check for understanding by reviewing children's responses to *Assessment Book* p. 35 or to the Lesson Review in the Student Edition.

Intervention Study Guide Use pp. 26–27 to review and reinforce lesson concepts as needed.

Universal Access

English Learners
Needs of Plants and Animals Explain to children that plants and animals need some of the same things to live, but some of their needs are different. Draw a Venn diagram on the board, labeling the parts *Plants*, *Plants and Animals*, and *Animals*.

RB4 ELD Reading
Beginning Write the words *air, water, sunlight,* and *food* on the board. Point to and read each word. Ask children if a plant or animal needs it to live. Write each need in the Venn diagram.

REI12 ELD Reading
Intermediate Ask children to respond with a sentence to the questions: "What do animals need to live? What do plants need to live?" Write each need in the Venn diagram. Have children explain why *water* and *air* are in each part of the diagram.

REA7 ELD Reading
Advanced Have children answer the question: "What might happen if there were no water in a bear's environment?"

Advanced Learners
Animal Needs Book Have children make a short book about an animal and what it needs to live. Encourage children to write many sentences and include information about where the animal lives and what it eats.

Extra Support
Animal Needs Mobile Have children make a mobile about the needs of an animal. Have them cut out a picture of an animal from a magazine and attach it to the top of a coat hanger. Then have them draw or find pictures of the things their animal needs to live. Have children cut out the pictures and then attach them to the hanger with string.

Special Needs
Observe and Care for a Class Pet Discuss with children how to take care of a pet. Help children make a list of the pet's needs. If possible, allow children to observe and take care of a class pet for a few days. After showing children how to care for the pet, invite them to take on these responsibilities.

1PS1.2 Statistics, Data Analysis, and Probability Represent and compare data (e.g., largest, smallest, most often, least often) by using pictures, bar graphs, tally charts, and picture graphs.

1IE4.5 Investigation and Experimentation Record observations and data with pictures, numbers, or written statements.

Objective Students use tally charts to represent and compare data.

Math in Science
 25 min

1. Build Background

Warm Up
Activate Prior Knowledge

▶ Draw five A's, three B's, and seven C's on the board. Ask children to tell which group is largest and which group is smallest. State that there are five A's and then ask children to suggest other ways they can represent the amount of five.

▶ Lead children to see that tally marks can be used to represent amounts.

2. Teach

Use Tally Marks

Show children the chart tallying trees and flowers. Have children count the trees in the picture. Help them understand how the chart is completed.

Ask: How many flowers are in the picture next to the chart?

Invite children to explain how they could record the number of flowers on the chart.

Share and Talk

Ask children to work in pairs to complete the chart on p. 89. Encourage them to discuss how they found the total number of each kind of animal.

eTools Use the Counters Tool to provide children with practice comparing numbers. Have children work in pairs. Ask one child to use the counters to create two sets. The sets should be different colors. Then have the other child state which set is larger. Have children switch roles and repeat the activity, this time asking which set is smaller.

Math in Science

TALLYING

You can use tally marks to record information.

1 | This is a tally mark.

2 ||||| These are 5 tally marks.

Plant	Tally	Total
Tree	|||||		6
Flower	||||| ||	7

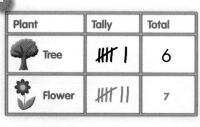

This chart shows how many trees are in the circle.

Make tally marks to record how many flowers are in the circle. Then write the total.

88

Make tally marks to record how many birds, lizards and insects there are in the picture. Then write the totals.

Animals	Tally	Total
Bird	IIII I	6
Lizard	III	3
Insect	IIII IIII	9

1. Which animal has the greatest number? 1. Insect

2. Which animal has the smallest number? 2. Lizard

Lab zone Take-Home Activity

Make a tally chart. Record the number of plants and animals you can find around home.

89

Take-Home Activity

Tips for Success
► Remind children to label the top of each column of their tally chart.
► Encourage children to write their tally marks neatly so that the information is accurate.

Mathematics Support

1PS1.2 Statistics, Data Analysis, and Probability

► Children may confuse tally marks with numerals. For example, they may think that two tally marks means the number 11.

► Use pictures to help children understand that each tally mark represents one unit. Draw five stick figures horizontally on the board. Then make a tally mark underneath each picture. Have children count the number of stick figures aloud. Write the number 5 to the right of them. Repeat for the tally marks.

Scaffolded Questions

Use the following guiding questions to monitor children's comprehension.

1 **Recall** What does each tally mark stand for? It stands for one of something.

2 **Apply** Have children use tally marks to record how many times you tap a pencil on a desk. Check children's answers.

3 **Compare** Suppose you have two sets of tally marks. How can you tell which set is larger? You can count the total number of marks in each set.

3. Summarize and Assess

QUICK Summary

► Tally marks are used to record information.

► You can use charts, graphs, or tally marks to compare amounts or numbers.

Assess

Check for understanding by reviewing responses to the questions on p. 89. Children may explain that they made a tally mark for each of a certain kind of animal they counted and then they found the total number of tally marks.

California Science

CONTENT STANDARDS FOCUS

1LS2.b **Life Sciences** Students know both plants and animals need water, animals need food, and plants need light.

1LS2.e **Life Sciences** Students know roots are associated with the intake of water and soil nutrients and green leaves are associated with making food from sunlight.

1IE4.b **Investigation and Experimentation** Record observations and data with pictures, numbers, or written statements.

Objective Students observe and record data to explain that plants need sunlight to grow.

Guided Inquiry

⏱ 15 min

1. Get Ready

Materials for Small Groups

2 clear plastic cups	water
grass seeds	pouring container
potting soil	washable paints (optional)

Materials listed in *italics* are kit materials.

▷ *QUICK* Plan

▶ Plant seeds in advance.

▶ Have children observe and draw the two plants, then separate them and observe daily for one week.

▶ This activity may be set up as a center activity.

2. What to Do

Preview

▶ 🔵9 **Active Glossary** Reinforce science vocabulary by encouraging children to use academic language from the chapter as they do the activity. For children who need extra support, post vocabulary cards (*Science Study Notebook*, pp. 33–34).

▶ Preview science content in Lessons 1 and 2.

Advance Preparation Plant seeds about 10 days in advance. Keep soil moist. Prepare 2 cups per group.

Tips

▶ Be careful not to over-water the seeds.

▶ In simple words explain to children that plants absorb sunlight which helps them meet their energy requirements. Point out how the plant grows toward the light to improve its ability to make food in its green leaves.

◢Lab zone ✦Guided Inquiry✦

Investigate Do plants need light?

Plants need water, air, sunlight, and nutrients. Find out what happens if plants do not get light.

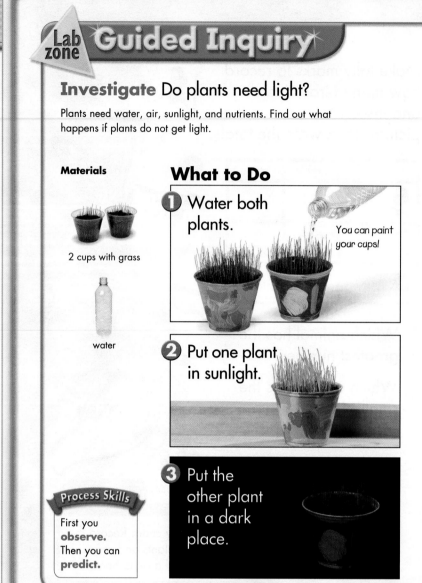

Materials

2 cups with grass

water

What to Do

① Water both plants.

You can paint your cups!

② Put one plant in sunlight.

③ Put the other plant in a dark place.

Process Skills

First you **observe.** Then you can **predict.**

90

Digital Classroom

🔵 **Activity Video** Prepare for and rehearse the activity before class.

🔵 **Printable Activity Rubric** Monitor children's progress using the Activity Rubric located at **www.sfsuccessnet.com**.

🔵 **Printable LabZone Activity** Provide children with additional activities located at **www.sfsuccessnet.com**.

Call **1-888-537-4908** with activity questions.

Record Data For each day of observation, have children draw a picture of each plant on the chart, side by side in their respective columns. Explain that each row of the chart will show how the plants look on a different day. Be sure to point out how many days have passed when returning from a weekend break. After a week of observation, ask children to describe the progress of the two plants.

Ask Questions Ask children which plant grew better. What happens if a plant does not get light?

4 How will the plants look after 1 week?
Observe the plants every day for 1 week.

	Sunlight	**Dark**
Day 1	The cup should look like the photo above.	The cup should look like the photo above.
Day 2	After 7 days the grass should be taller and green.	After 7 days the grass should be the same height as day 1 and brown.

5 Fill in the chart. Record your observations. Draw pictures. Write what you see.

Explain Your Results
1. Which grew better? Draw. Grass in the sunlight.
2. **Predict** What happens if a plant does not get light? It will die.

Go Further
What will happen if you move the plant from the dark place to a sunny place? Try it and find out.

91

3. Explain Your Results

Science Study Notebook

Printable Resources Activity Recording Sheet Discuss the results of the activity by reviewing completed pp. 41–42. Ask volunteers to tell what they observed. Discuss why plants need light to grow.

Activity Rubric Use *Science Study Notebook Teacher's Guide* p. T25 to evaluate children's work.

Go Further
▶ Discuss what children think might happen if the weakened plant is moved back into the sunlight. Move it alongside the other plant and observe them as a class.

▶ Collect other questions about plant growth and post them on the bulletin board. Encourage children to investigate these questions on their own.

Big Idea	**Teacher Background**
Plants need light to grow and stay healthy.	▶ Plants create food out of carbon dioxide and water through the process of photosynthesis, which requires energy from sunlight. This energy is absorbed by the leaves, which are green because of the light-capturing pigment chlorophyll. ▶ If the leaves are denied exposure to sunlight, photosynthesis cannot take place and the plant starves.

1. Lesson Summaries

▶ Review the lesson summaries on p. 92 by asking children each lesson focus question and encouraging them to answer using their own words. If children struggle to answer, have them look at the lesson picture to review the key concepts.

▶ Divide the class into three groups and assign each group one lesson from the chapter. Children should reread and review the material in their assigned lesson.

▶ Have each group work together to develop a short skit for their assigned lesson. Encourage creativity. Group members can decide who will do what to act out living things. Be sure children include the chapter's topics and vocabulary terms in their skits.

2. Reinforce Concepts

▶ Have each group present the skit to the class. Encourage groups to give details that show how the topics in their lesson relate to the chapter's Big Idea. Invite children to discuss the skits of the other groups.

▶ After the groups present their skits, as a class talk about how each skit helped children understand the chapter.

▶ Suggest to children that they think about each of the skits to prepare for the Chapter 3 Review/Test (pp. 94–95).

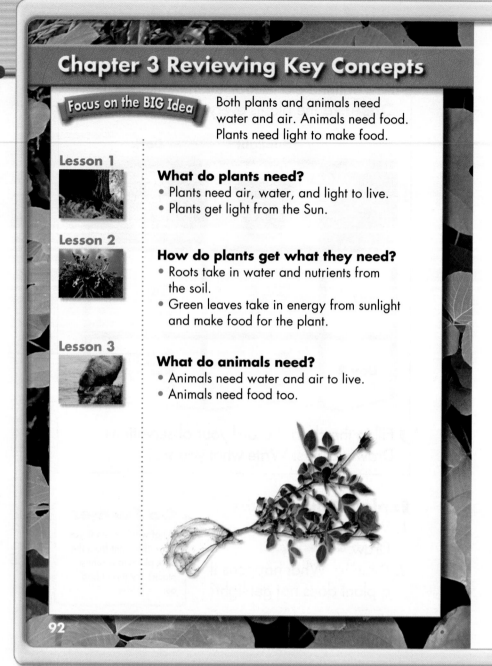

Chapter 3 Reviewing Key Concepts

Focus on the BIG Idea Both plants and animals need water and air. Animals need food. Plants need light to make food.

Lesson 1

What do plants need?
• Plants need air, water, and light to live.
• Plants get light from the Sun.

Lesson 2

How do plants get what they need?
• Roots take in water and nutrients from the soil.
• Green leaves take in energy from sunlight and make food for the plant.

Lesson 3

What do animals need?
• Animals need water and air to live.
• Animals need food too.

92

Further Learning

Meet individually with each group to discuss the content of each topic and the roles children might play in the skit. For example, one child can be a plant, another can be water, air, and so on. Consider having an advanced learner in each group be the narrator to help explain what is happening in the skit.

Cross-Curricular Links

English–Language Arts

Building Vocabulary

Look again at pages 74 and 75. Find the picture for the word **leaves.**

Write about the color of these leaves. Tell what leaves do for the plant.

Mathematics

Planning a Garden

Suppose you have 8 plants to make a garden.

Make a picture to show how you can put all the plants in 2 rows. Each row should have the same number of plants.

Challenge!

Visual and Performing Arts

Drawing a Leaf

Look at a leaf. Draw and color a picture of the leaf.

Make your picture the same size, shape, and color as the leaf.

Health

Eating Vegetables

You need good food to stay healthy. Vegetables help you get the vitamins you need.

Research and make a list of vegetables to eat.

93

3. Chapter Focus Questions

▶ Direct children's attention to the Big Idea on p. 92. Have children give a summary about the Big Idea orally. Encourage them to use vocabulary terms and other academic language from the chapter. Answers will vary.

▶ Have children draw a plant and label the parts. Under each label have them tell what the plant part does. Answers will vary.

Ask:

▶ Do you think plants or animals have more needs? Why do you think so? Answers will vary. Encourage children to use knowledge from the chapter to explain.

Cross-Curricular Links

English-Language Arts
Building Vocabulary

1WA2.2 **Writing Applications** Answers will vary. See the Writing Rubric for Building Vocabulary to the right for support on scoring children's writing.

Mathematics
Planning a Garden

1NS1.3 **Number Sense** Pictures should show two rows of plants with four plants in each row.

Visual and Performing Arts
Drawing a Leaf

Check children's drawings for comparability of size, shape, and color to the leaf.

Health
Challenge Eating Vegetables

Answers will vary. Encourage children to include a variety of vegetables.

Writing Rubric for Building Vocabulary

4	Child writes a detailed, accurate description of the leaves' color and tells what leaves do for the plant. There are few, if any, capitalization or punctuation errors.
3	Child correctly describes the leaves' color and tells what leaves are for. There are a few errors in the use of capital letters and end marks.
2	Child describes the leaves' color. The function of leaves is not explained or is explained incorrectly. There are many errors in the use of capital letters and end marks.
1	Child writes unfocused and unclear sentences. Errors in the use of capital letters and end marks make comprehension difficult.

Vocabulary

1. B

2. A

Think About It

3. Plants and animals are two kinds of living things.

4. The roots of a plant take in water and nutrients from the soil.

5. Animals need to eat food to live.

6. Animals need food, air, and water to live.

7. **Infer** If a plant does not get the light and water it needs, it will not grow well and might die.

Refer to side columns for answers.

Chapter 3 Review/Test

Vocabulary

Which picture goes with each word?

1. roots (page 83)

2. leaves (page 83)

Think About It

3. What are two kinds of living things? (pages 79, 86)

4. What part of the plant takes in water and nutrients from the soil? (page 83)

5. Why do animals need to eat? (page 87)

6. ✎ **Writing in Science** Name three things animals need to live. (page 87)

7. **Process Skills** **Infer** What might happen if a plant does not get the light and water it needs? (page 80)

94

Universal Access

Special Needs

Accommodate individual children as needed to distinguish between lack of content knowledge and physical or linguistic limitations.

Common Accommodations

▶ Provide additional time.

▶ **AudioText** Read the test. An audio recording of the Chapter Review/Test is available on AudioText.

▶ Allow children who have difficulty writing to audio record answers.

Assessment Resources

Printable Chapter Test
Assessment Book pp. 37–40

Success Tracker
Use this flexible, online assessment system to track Adequate Yearly Progress and provide intervention. Find it at **www.sfsuccessnet.com**.

Printable Student Progress Report
TE pp. EMxvii–EMxviii

Show What You Know
TE pp. 166–167

ExamView
Customizable Chapter 3 Test

MindPoint QuizShow
Chapter 3 review in game format

Relate Prior Knowledge

8. Possible answer:

Tell what I know.

Green leaves take in sunlight.

8. **Relate Prior Knowledge** What part of the plant takes in sunlight? (page 85)

Plants have parts that help them live and grow.

Tell what I know.

California Standards Practice

Write the letter of the correct answer.

9. What part of the plant makes food?

A flowers

B leaves

C stems

D roots

10. What are nutrients?

A parts of a plant that take in water

B materials that living things need

C living things

D light from the Sun

95

California Standards Practice

9. B

10. B

Intervention and Reteaching

California Science CONTENT STANDARDS FOCUS	Review Items	Student Edition	Teacher's Edition Resources			Ancillary Resources	
			Scaffolded Questions	Extend Vocab	Diagnostic Check	Intervention Study Guide	Science Study Notebook
1LS2.b Life Sciences Students know both plants and animals need water, animals need food, and plants need light.	3, 5, 6, 7	78–81, 86–87	79, 81, 86	79, 81, 87	79	22–23, 26–27	31–32, 33–34, 36, 38, 40, 41–42
1LS2.e Life Sciences Students know roots are associated with the intake of water and soil nutrients and green leaves are associated with making food from sunlight.	1, 2, 3, 4, 8, 9, 10	82–85	83, 85	83, 85	83	24–25	31–32, 33–34, 39, 41–42

California English-Language Arts
CONTENT STANDARDS FOCUS

1RW1.16 Word Analysis, Fluency, and Systematic Vocabulary Development Read aloud with fluency in a manner that sounds like natural speech.

Objective Students read about and discuss what naturalists do.

Career
25 min

1. Build Background

Warm Up
Activate Prior Knowledge

▶ Have children discuss ways that people help animals.

▶ Ask children what jobs they can name where people help animals. Veterinarians, dog trainers, and zoo-keepers help animals.

▶ Write children's responses in a chart and revisit at the end of the discussion.

2. Teach

Share and Talk

Read p. 96 together. Then have children write questions they would like to ask a naturalist. Encourage children to include questions such as:

▶ What plants and animals do you try to help?

▶ What kinds of things do you do when you're working?

Work with English learners to write a few simple sentences about naturalists. Then have children read the sentences aloud.

3. Summarize and Assess

▶ Work with children to create a word web that includes facts about naturalists' work to save California condors.

▶ After they have created their word webs, encourage children to create ideas for a class story that tells about a naturalist working to save California condors. Record their suggestions and read the story back to children.

Career

Naturalist

Read Aloud

Naturalists help animals and plants. Some naturalists help the California condor.

The California condor is the largest bird in North America. Many years ago, there were about 25 California condors left in the wild.

Naturalists began a program to add more condors to the wild. Now there are about 125 California condors living in the wild.

Lab zone Take-Home Activity

Tell your family about how naturalists have added to the number of California condors living in the wild.

96

Big Idea	Teacher Background
Naturalists help animals and plants.	▶ John Muir was a prominent naturalist. He was devoted to conserving plants and animals. In 1876, Muir urged the United States government to embrace conservation of the nation's forests. Through his work, the Sequoia and Yosemite National Parks were established in 1890.
	▶ Naturalists and biologists started captive breeding programs in which wild condors were captured and protected in zoos. The San Diego Wild Animal Park and the Los Angeles Zoo are two sites that have breeding populations. By 1991, a number of California condors that had been bred in captivity were reintroduced to the wild.

Take-Home Activity

Tip for Success

▶ Invite children to summarize the main ideas they learned from the feature on naturalists.

Chapter 4

Environments

1LS2.0 Plants and animals meet their needs in different ways. As a basis for understanding this concept:

1LS2.a Students know different plants and animals inhabit different kinds of environments and have external features that help them thrive in different kinds of places.

1IE4.0 Scientific progress is made by asking meaningful questions and conducting careful investigations. As a basis for understanding this concept and addressing the content in the other three strands, students should develop their own questions and perform investigations.

1IE4.a Draw pictures that portray some features of the thing being described.

1IE4.b Record observations and data with pictures, numbers, or written statements.

1IE4.c Record observations on a bar graph.

Standards Focus Questions

- What is an environment?
- What lives in a forest?
- What lives in an ocean?
- What lives in a desert?

LESSON PLANNING GUIDE

LESSON TITLES AND PACING

California Science CONTENT STANDARDS

Environments

Lab zone ▶ **Directed Inquiry**

⏱ 10 min

Explore
Where do animals live?
p. 100

1LS2.a Students know different plants and animals inhabit different kinds of environments and have external features that help them thrive in different kinds of places.

1IE4.a Draw pictures that portray some features of the thing being described.

LESSON 1

What is an environment?
pp. 102–105

⏱ 30 min

1LS2.a Students know different plants and animals inhabit different kinds of environments and have external features that help them thrive in different kinds of places.

LESSON 2

What lives in a forest?
pp. 106–109

⏱ 30 min

1LS2.a Students know different plants and animals inhabit different kinds of environments and have external features that help them thrive in different kinds of places.

LESSON 3

What lives in an ocean?
pp. 110–113

⏱ 30 min

1LS2.a Students know different plants and animals inhabit different kinds of environments and have external features that help them thrive in different kinds of places.

LESSON 4

What lives in a desert?
pp. 114–117

⏱ 30 min

1LS2.a Students know different plants and animals inhabit different kinds of environments and have external features that help them thrive in different kinds of places.

Lab zone ▶ **Guided Inquiry**

⏱ 20 min

Investigate
How do some desert leaves hold water?
pp. 120–121

1LS2.a Students know different plants and animals inhabit different kinds of environments and have external features that help them thrive in different kinds of places.

1IE4.a Draw pictures that portray some features of the thing being described. (also **1IE4.b**)

Reviewing Key Concepts

⏱ 25 min

Review and assess each science content standard from the chapter as listed above.

Chapter 4 Review/Test
pp. 122–125

VOCAB/SKILLS	ASSESSMENT/INTERVENTION
Process Skill: Classify	• **Explain Your Results,** SE p. 100 • **Activity Recording Sheet,** *Science Study Notebook* p. 48 • **Activity Rubric,** *Science Study Notebook Teacher's Guide* p. T26
environment	• **Scaffolded Questions,** TE pp. 103, 105 • **Chapter Study Guide,** *Science Study Notebook* pp. 43–44 • **Lesson Study Guide,** *Science Study Notebook* p. 50 • **Lesson Quiz,** *Assessment Book* p. 43
forest	• **Scaffolded Questions,** TE pp. 107, 109 • **Lesson Study Guide,** *Science Study Notebook* p. 51 • **Lesson Quiz,** *Assessment Book* p. 44
ocean	• **Scaffolded Questions,** TE pp. 111, 113 • **Lesson Study Guide,** *Science Study Notebook* p. 52 • **Lesson Quiz,** *Assessment Book* p. 45
desert	• **Scaffolded Questions,** TE pp. 115, 117 • **Lesson Study Guide,** *Science Study Notebook* p. 53 • **Lesson Quiz,** *Assessment Book* p. 46
Process Skills: Collect Data Observe	• **Explain Your Results,** SE p. 121 • **Activity Recording Sheet,** *Science Study Notebook* pp. 54–55 • **Activity Rubric,** *Science Study Notebook Teacher's Guide* p. T27
	• **Intervention and Reteaching Chart,** TE p. 125 • **Chapter Test,** *Assessment Book* pp. 47–50 • **Success Tracker** www.sfsuccessnet.com

DIGITAL CLASSROOM

 Printable Resources
• *Science Study Notebook* pp. 43–55
• Graphic Organizer, TE p. EMxix
• *Intervention Study Guide* pp. 28–35
• *Assessment Book* pp. 41–50
• *Teacher's Activity Guide* pp. 18–19
• LabZone Activities

 AudioText
Unit B, Chapter 4

 eTools
Spreadsheet/Data/Grapher

 Activity Videos
Unit B, Chapter 4

UNIVERSAL ACCESS

English Learners
TE pp. 103, 107, 111, 115

Special Needs
TE pp. 104, 108, 112, 116

Advanced Learners
TE pp. 104, 108, 112, 116

Extra Support
TE pp. 105, 109, 113, 117

CONTENT READERS

 The *Science Content Readers Teacher's Guide* includes California Science Content Standards.

 Below-Level   On-Level Above-Level

  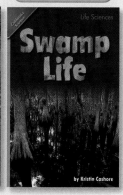

DIFFERENTIATED INSTRUCTION

Content Readers deliver the same standards, vocabulary, concepts, and skills as the chapter and can be used for original instruction, reteaching, and enrichment.

Below-Level

On-Level

Summary

Animals and plants live in environments. Environments provide plants and animals with air, food, and water. There are different types of environments. This book focuses on forest, desert, and ocean environments. In each type of environment, there are plants and animals especially suited to that environment.

Summary

Animals and plants live in environments. Environments provide plants and animals with air, food, and water. There are different types of environments. This book focuses on forest, desert, and ocean environments. In each type of environment, there are plants and animals especially suited to that environment. For example, in the desert, some plants have seeds that resist heat very well. In the ocean, whales have baleen that enables them to scoop up krill and other small organisms from the sea floor. In the forest, bobcats have strong legs and good hearing to catch prey.

Above-Level

California Science

Life Sciences

Swamp Life

by Kristin Cashore

Summary

Different plants and animals live in different environments. Swamps are wet environments. The plants and animals that live in swamps do well in wet environments. Cypress and mangrove trees have long roots to reach through the water. Other plants float on the water. Swamp plants provide many animals with food and shelter. Animals such as turtles, snakes, lizards, caimans, and alligators swim in swamp water. Animals such as frogs, bobcats, and raccoons climb in the trees. Wading birds with long legs and necks also live in swamps.

Extended Vocabulary for Above-Level Content Reader

dangerous	swamp
float	wading
prey	waterlogged

www.sfsuccessnet.com

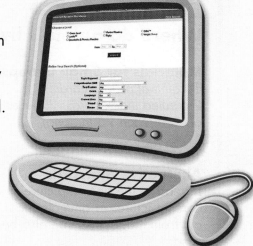

Use the online database to search for additional content readers by title, content, and target reading skill.

▶ To use the online database, go to **www.sfsuccessnet.com**, and enter your User ID and password from your Teacher Access Pack.

▶ Once logged in, enter the database.

▶ Choose a reading level or a range, or choose other search criteria.

▶ Specify content area, comprehension skill, and/or theme.

▶ Assign text, matching appropriate reading levels for children.

▶ Assign readers to individual children.

▶ Listen to each selection.

▶ Download and print.

▶ Print lesson plans and worksheets for each reader.

Lab zone Directed Inquiry

1LS2.a **Life Sciences** Students know different plants and animals inhabit different kinds of environments and have external features that help them thrive in different kinds of places.

1IE4.a **Investigation and Experimentation** Draw pictures that portray some features of the thing being described.

Explore  10 min
Where do animals live? p. 100

Materials for Small Groups
10 animal picture cards;
2 unruled index cards; 2 pieces
of yarn (each 96 in. long)

Materials listed in *italics* are kit materials.

Alternative Materials
Instead of the animal picture cards, pictures of animals cut out from magazines can also be used.

Advance Preparation Have children make word cards by labeling the two cards *Land* and *Water*. Cut two 8-foot lengths of yarn for each group.

Teaching Tips Challenge children to name as many of the animals as they can. If children are uncertain where an animal lives, encourage them to observe its picture more closely. How do they imagine it would move? Does it have body parts that would help it move in the water? on land? When children have sorted all the cards, ask children what other animals they can think of, then encourage them to classify those animals as well. Describe the features that allow those animals to live on land or in the water, and then have children draw the new animals.

What to Expect Children should understand that all animals have features that help them thrive on the land or in the water.

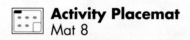 **Activity Video**
Unit B, Chapter 4

Activity Placemat
Mat 8

Lab zone Guided Inquiry

1LS2.a **Life Sciences** Students know different plants and animals inhabit different kinds of environments and have external features that help them thrive in different kinds of places.

1IE4.a **Investigation and Experimentation** Draw pictures that portray some features of the thing being described. (also **1IE4.b**)

Investigate ⏱ 20 min
How do some desert leaves hold water? pp. 120–121

Materials for Small Groups
desert leaf shapes (Activity Master 1); green construction paper (1 sheet); *spray bottle (16 oz)*; *waxed paper (12 × 12 in. sheet)*; water (for spray bottle); plate or tray (optional)

Materials listed in *italics* are kit materials.

Alternative Materials
Children may use moistened paper towels to wet leaves. If a sunny place is not available, place the leaves under a lamp with a 40 watt bulb.

Advance Preparation Cut waxed paper into 12 x 12 in. squares. Copy Activity Master 1 (*Science Study Notebook Teacher's Guide* p. T58) onto green construction paper. Cut out two paper leaves for each group. Fill the spray bottle.

Teaching Tips Children can place their leaves on a plate or tray before spraying with water. Make sure children wet both leaves evenly. Have them fold wax paper over one leaf shape. In this activity, the waxed paper is like the waxy covering of a desert leaf.

What to Expect The paper leaf covered in waxed paper will remain damp after 20 minutes, while the paper leaf without waxed paper will be dry.

 **Activity Video**
Unit B, Chapter 4

 Activity Placemat
Mat 9

Additional Activity Resources

The following resources are available for activities found in the Student Edition.

 Printable Resources

▸ *Science Study Notebook*
   • Activity Recording Sheets
     Recording sheets provide structure to help children record data from each activity.
   • Activity Rubrics
     Teachers can monitor children's progress using the Activity Rubric in the *Science Study Notebook Teacher's Guide*.
▸ *Teacher's Activity Guide* For detailed information about Inquiry Activities, access the *Teacher's Activity Guide* at **www.sfsuccessnet.com**.

 Activity Videos
Prepare for and rehearse each activity before class by watching a video of the activity.

> *"As students progress through the three stages of inquiry, support from the teacher diminishes and student ownership increases."*
>
> —Dr. Karen Ostlund, UTeach, College of Natural Sciences, The University of Texas at Austin

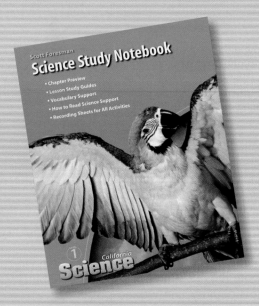

▶ **Chapter Study Guide**
Children preview and organize the key concepts in the chapter.

▶ **Chapter Vocabulary Cards** Children cut out cards to use with suggested strategies in the Teacher's Edition.

▶ **Chapter Vocabulary Preview** Children are introduced to science words.

▶ **How to Read Science** Children record answers for the Student Edition page.

▶ **Lesson Study Guides** Children practice note-taking as they learn key concepts while reading.

▶ **Inquiry Activities** *Science Study Notebook Teacher's Guide* provides an Activity Rubric to evaluate children's progress.

▶ **Printable Resources** All pages of the *Science Study Notebook* are available to purchasers of Scott Foresman California Science ©2008 at www.sfsuccessnet.com.

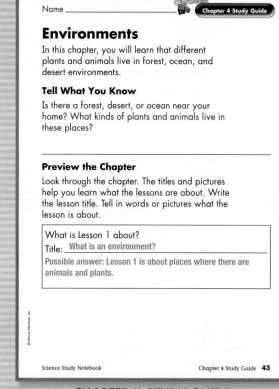

CHAPTER 4 STUDY GUIDE
Science Study Notebook, p. 43

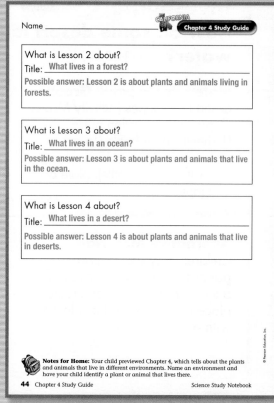

CHAPTER 4 STUDY GUIDE
Science Study Notebook, p. 44

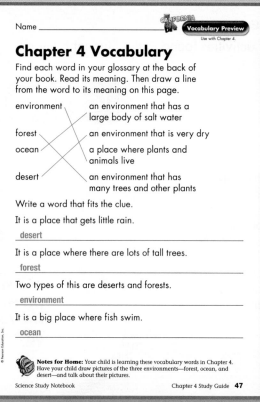

CHAPTER 4 VOCABULARY PREVIEW
Science Study Notebook, p. 47

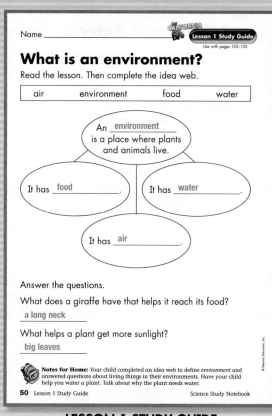

LESSON 1 STUDY GUIDE
Science Study Notebook, p. 50

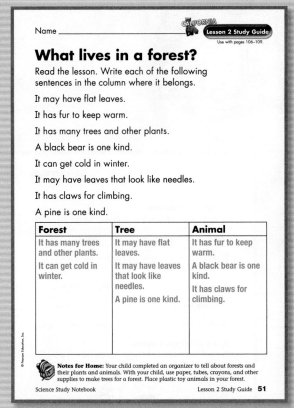

LESSON 2 STUDY GUIDE
Science Study Notebook, p. 51

Name _____

What lives in a forest?

Read the lesson. Write each of the following sentences in the column where it belongs.

It may have flat leaves.

It has fur to keep warm.

It has many trees and other plants.

A black bear is one kind.

It can get cold in winter.

It may have leaves that look like needles.

It has claws for climbing.

A pine is one kind.

Forest	Tree	Animal
It has many trees and other plants.	It may have flat leaves.	It has fur to keep warm.
It can get cold in winter.	It may have leaves that look like needles.	A black bear is one kind.
	A pine is one kind.	It has claws for climbing.

Notes for Home: Your child completed an organizer to tell about forests and their plants and animals. With your child, use paper, tubes, crayons, and other supplies to make trees for a forest. Place plastic toy animals in your forest.

Science Study Notebook   Lesson 2 Study Guide **51**

LESSON 3 STUDY GUIDE
Science Study Notebook, p. 52

Name _____

What lives in an ocean?

Read the lesson. Tell what an ocean is. Write your answer.

An ocean is a large body of salt water.

Look at the names. Circle plants and animals that belong in the ocean environment. Draw a line through the plants and animals that do not live there.

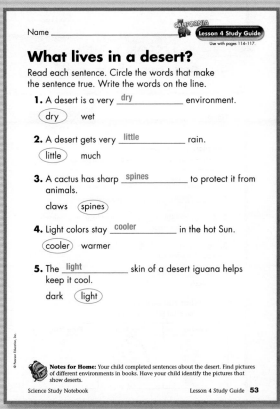

Notes for Home: Your child identified plants and animals that live in the ocean. Take turns with your child naming a plant or an animal and telling whether it lives in the ocean environment.

52 Lesson 3 Study Guide   Science Study Notebook

Name _____

What lives in a desert?

Read each sentence. Circle the words that make the sentence true. Write the words on the line.

1. A desert is a very _dry_ environment.
(dry) wet

2. A desert gets very _little_ rain.
(little) much

3. A cactus has sharp _spines_ to protect it from animals.
claws (spines)

4. Light colors stay _cooler_ in the hot Sun.
(cooler) warmer

5. The _light_ skin of a desert iguana helps keep it cool.
dark (light)

Notes for Home: Your child completed sentences about the desert. Find pictures of different environments in books. Have your child identify the pictures that show deserts.

Science Study Notebook   Lesson 4 Study Guide **53**

LESSON 4 STUDY GUIDE
Science Study Notebook, p. 53

Scott Foresman
Assessment Book
• Chapter Pretests
• Lesson Quizzes
• Chapter and Unit Tests
• Summative Test

California
Science

Printable Resources All pages of the *Assessment Book* are available to purchasers of Scott Foresman California Science ©2008 at **www.sfsuccessnet.com**.

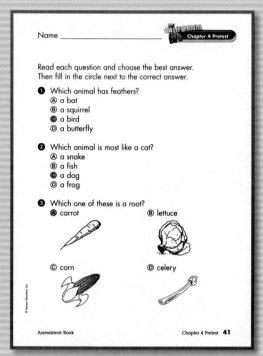

CHAPTER 4 PRETEST
Assessment Book, p. 41

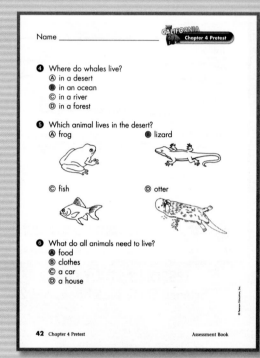

CHAPTER 4 PRETEST
Assessment Book, p. 42

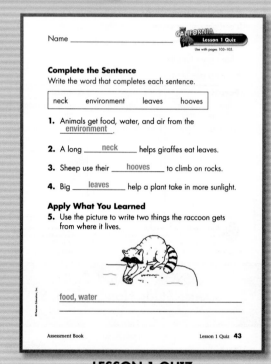

LESSON 1 QUIZ
Assessment Book, p. 43

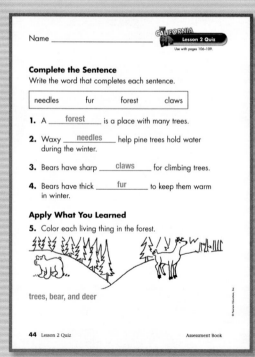

LESSON 2 QUIZ
Assessment Book, p. 44

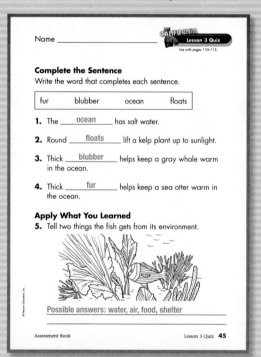

LESSON 3 QUIZ
Assessment Book, p. 45

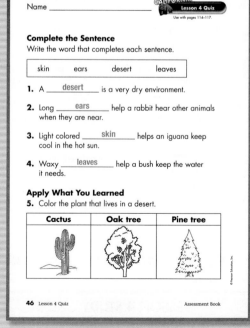

LESSON 4 QUIZ
Assessment Book, p. 46

Entry-Level Assessment	Progress-Monitoring Assessment		Summative Assessment

Entry-Level Assessment

▶ **Assessment Book:**
Chapter 4 Pretest

Progress-Monitoring Assessment

Ongoing Assessment
▶ **Student Edition:**
Checkpoint and Lesson Review questions
▶ **Teacher's Edition:**
Diagnostic Check and Scaffolded Questions
▶ **Assessment Book:**
Lesson Quizzes

▶ **DIGITAL** **Success Tracker**
Chapter 4 online assessment and reteaching

Formal Assessment
▶ **Student Edition:**
Chapter 4 Review/Test
▶ **DIGITAL** **ExamView**
Customizable Chapter 4 Test

Summative Assessment

▶ **Student Edition:**
Unit B California Standards Practice
▶ **Assessment Book:**
Chapter 4 Test
Unit B Test
Summative Test

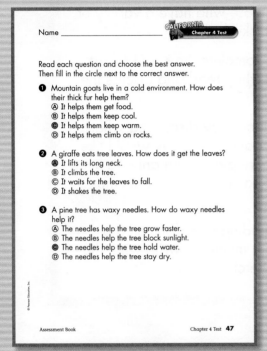

CHAPTER 4 TEST
Assessment Book, p. 47

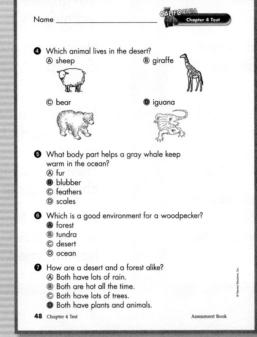

CHAPTER 4 TEST
Assessment Book, p. 48

CHAPTER 4 TEST
Assessment Book, p. 49

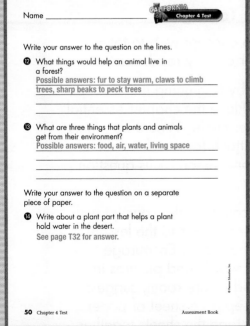

CHAPTER 4 TEST
Assessment Book, p. 50

Strategies

Use these suggested strategies to help you customize instruction for children with individual needs.

Strategies for
English Learners

Words in Action

▶ Model, demonstrate, or pantomime word meanings. Support your presentations with visuals, songs, items to touch, and other appropriate uses of the five senses.

▶ **Beginning** Hold up one object or show one action. Say its name, and use it in a simple sentence. Have children repeat.

▶ **Intermediate** Demonstrate the meanings of two to four related objects or actions. Graphic organizers or diagrams may be helpful. Have children use the words in talks with a partner.

▶ **Advanced** Use pantomime to act out various words. Encourage children to describe the actions. Then help them write the words in their word collection books.

Strategies for
Special Needs

K-W-L Chart

▶ Organize children into study groups. Construct the groups so that children with special needs are grouped with those who have a variety of learning styles and skill levels.

▶ Have each group complete the K-W-L Chart on TE p. EMxxv as they read and discuss the chapter.

▶ Instruct groups to begin by discussing what they already know and what they would like to know about where plants and animals live. Have one child in each group serve as the chart recorder.

▶ After they finish reading and discussing a section, have group members write what they have learned on the chart.

Strategies for
Advanced Learners

Independent Reading

▶ Review with children the chapter essential question: *Where do plants and animals live?* Have children identify the key concepts in the chapter.

▶ Invite children to choose a book on one of the topics in the chapter that is of interest to them for independent reading. Some possible suggestions include *African Animals* by Caroline Arnold (ISBN 0-6881-4115-3) and *Humphrey the Lost Whale: A True Story* by Wendy Tokuda and Richard Hall (ISBN 0-89346-270-5).

▶ Have children prepare a book review, an oral presentation, or a drawing about their selected book.

Strategies for
Extra Support

Note-Taking

▶ Have children use a concept web to take notes on the chapter as they read.

▶ Model the strategy by beginning the concept web on the board. Place the chapter essential question in the center circle: *Where do plants and animals live?* Attach four circles with spokes, and place one lesson focus question in each circle.

▶ Instruct children to complete the concept web by adding spokes and circles to the lesson focus questions as they read. Encourage children to use both words and pictures in their webs. To provide more room, suggest that children use a separate sheet of paper for each lesson and tape the sheets together once they have finished.

Integrated Universal Access

	English Learners	Special Needs	Advanced Learners	Extra Support
1LS2.a Students know different plants and animals inhabit different kinds of environments and have external features that help them thrive in different kinds of places.	**Describe an Environment** TE p. 103	**Sounds from Different Environments** TE p. 104	**Research Local Animals** TE p. 104	**Make a Table** TE p. 105
	Describe Features of Forest Animals TE p. 107	**Examine Tree Leaves** TE p. 108	**Research Rain Forest Plants and Animals** TE p. 108	**Dress for Cold Experiments** TE p. 109
	Life in the Ocean TE p. 111	**How Ocean Animals Move** TE p. 112	**Research Endangered Species** TE p. 112	**Examine Pictures of Sea Animals** TE p. 113
	Discuss External Features of Animals TE p. 115	**Touch the Desert** TE p. 116	**Research Camels** TE p. 116	**Understand How the Iguana Keeps Cool** TE p. 117

California English-Language Arts
CONTENT STANDARDS FOCUS

1RW1.0 Word Analysis, Fluency, and Systematic Vocabulary Development Students understand the basic features of reading. They select patterns and know how to translate them into spoken language by using phonics, syllabication, and word parts. They apply this knowledge to achieve fluent oral and silent reading.

Objective Students determine meaning and increase vocabulary as they read science.

Focus on the **Big Idea** 🕐 **20 min**

Chapter 4 Vocabulary Terms

environment, p. 103   ocean, p. 110
forest, p. 106   desert, p. 114

DIGITAL 📄 **Printable Pretest** Assess children's background knowledge with Chapter 4 Pretest on *Assessment Book* pp. 41–42.

1. Build Background

Warm Up
Activate Prior Knowledge

▶ Ask children the essential question, *Where do plants and animals live?* Save responses for later in the chapter.

▶ Ask children to name some different environments or habitats where animals live. List their responses on the board.

2. Introduce Vocabulary

Preview Terms

Draw a word web on the board and use it to focus children's attention on science vocabulary as they read Chapter 4.

▶ Many science vocabulary words are abstract. Use the pictures and labels on these pages to help you open a discussion about science concepts and build academic language.

▶ List the vocabulary terms on the board. Have children pronounce each word as you write it on the word web.

▶ Discuss the meaning of each word and how it relates to where plants and animals live.

Focus on the BIG Idea

Where do plants and animals live?

environment

ocean

forest

98 DIGITAL 9

Big Idea | Teacher Background

Different plants and animals inhabit different kinds of environments and have external features that help them thrive in different kinds of places.

▶ Plants and animals have developed a variety of adaptations to help them survive in their environments. These adaptations include specialized body parts that children can see and readily discuss, relating structural form and function.

▶ Some of these body parts or external features help the plants or animals find food or shelter. Others help the plants or animals protect themselves or reproduce.

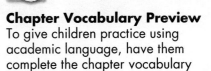

Chapter 4 Vocabulary

desert

99

Share and Talk

Use questions such as the following to help children clarify their understanding of vocabulary terms.

▶ How are the vocabulary terms *ocean*, *forest*, and *desert* related? Each of them is a type of environment in which an animal can live.

▶ What is the environment like where you live? Answers will vary.

Science Study Notebook

Printable Resources

Chapter Vocabulary Preview

To give children practice using academic language, have them complete the chapter vocabulary preview on p. 47.

Vocabulary Cards Have children use the vocabulary cards on pp. 45–46 to draw a picture. Children should choose two vocabulary cards and draw a picture of each vocabulary term.

3. Practice

Active Glossary Reinforce science vocabulary and concepts with Active Glossary animations.

Vocabulary Strategy

Synonyms and Antonyms Tell children that synonyms are words that have the same meaning. The words *big* and *large* are synonyms.

Ask: What is a synonym for the word *environment*? Possible answer: A place, an area, and a habitat can mean the same as the word *environment*. Help children understand that the words *environment* and *habitat* both refer to places where plants and animals can live.

California Science

CONTENT STANDARDS FOCUS

1LS2.a **Life Sciences** Students know different plants and animals inhabit different kinds of environments and have external features that help them thrive in different kinds of places.

1IE4.a **Investigation and Experimentation** Draw pictures that portray some features of the thing being described.

Objective Students classify animals as living on land or in the sea.

Directed Inquiry ⏱ 10 min

1. Get Ready

Materials for Small Groups
animal picture cards
2 blank index cards
yarn
Materials listed in *italics* are kit materials.

2. What to Do

Preview
▸ Conduct an inventory of materials with children. For English Learners, solicit alternative names for items in their home language. Post the names of materials and other academic language, such as *classify*.

▸ You may wish to preview science content in Lesson 1.

Advance Preparation
Cut two 8-foot lengths of yarn for each group.

Tips
▸ Have children make word cards by labeling the two blank cards *Land* and *Water*.

▸ Have children think of body parts the animals have to help classify them.

3. Explain Your Results

Science Study Notebook
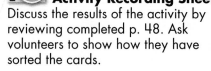
Printable Resources Activity Recording Sheet
Discuss the results of the activity by reviewing completed p. 48. Ask volunteers to show how they have sorted the cards.

Activity Rubric Use *Science Study Notebook Teacher's Guide* p. T26 to evaluate children's work.

Lab zone Directed Inquiry

Explore Where do animals live?

Materials

yarn

picture cards

word cards

What to Do

① Make 2 yarn circles.

② Sort the picture cards. Which animals live on land? Which animals live on water?

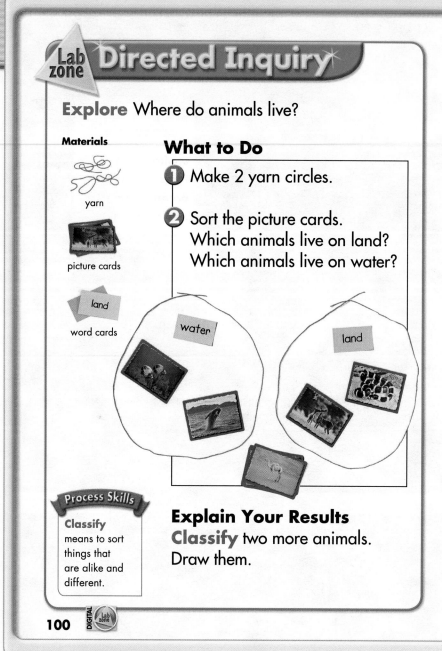

Process Skills

Classify means to sort things that are alike and different.

Explain Your Results
Classify two more animals. Draw them.

100

Digital Classroom

Activity Video Prepare for and rehearse the activity before class.

Printable Activity Rubric Monitor children's progress using the Activity Rubric located at **www.sfsuccessnet.com**.

Printable LabZone Activity Provide children with additional activities located at **www.sfsuccessnet.com**.

Call **1-888-537-4908** with activity questions.

Big Idea	**Teacher Background**
Animals can be classified by the places they live.	▸ Almost every environment on Earth is home to some form of life. Scientists classify animals in a variety of ways, including by habitat. ▸ Animals are adapted to their environments and often reflect them as a result. Because land and sea pose such different challenges to life, they are home to very different kinds of animals.

How to Read Science

Use Context Clues

Pictures can give you clues about what you read.

Science Story

Different animals live in different places. The sea otter has thick fur that keeps it warm in water. The black bear has thick fur that keeps it warm on land.

Apply It!
Classify Where can different animals with fur live?

101

English-Language Arts Support

1RC2.4 **Reading Comprehension**

▶ **Printable Graphic Organizer** Use *Graphic Organizer 1* (TE p. EMxix) with children to help them understand what they read.

▶ To help meet the needs of children whose reading skills are below grade level, have children work with a partner to compare the information in the article to the information in the pictures. Have children underline facts in the article that are also evident in the pictures. Then discuss how the pictures can help them understand the text.

California English-Language Arts
CONTENT STANDARDS FOCUS

1RC2.4 **Reading Comprehension** Use context to resolve ambiguities about word and sentence meanings.

Objective Students use context clues to assign meanings to unfamiliar words in a science story.

How to Read Science ⟨ 25 min

1. Build Background

Comprehension Skill: Use Context Clues

Children will often encounter unfamiliar words when reading about a new topic. Tell children that one way to figure out what an unfamiliar word means is to look at the pictures that go with a story and use clues from the pictures to determine the meaning of the word. Explain that another way is to read the words that surround the unfamiliar word.

Ask: What can you learn about an animal by looking at a picture of it? You can learn about an animal's size, shape, covering, and so on.

2. Teach

Science Story

Direct children to look at the pictures on p. 101 as they read the story. Point out how the pictures give clues about words that are used in the story.

Science Study Notebook

Printable Recording Sheet To help children understand how to use pictures as context clues, have them complete the How to Read Science recording sheet on p. 49.

3. Summarize and Assess

Apply It!

Using context clues involves using pictures to better understand what you read. Work with children to complete the graphic organizer using the information from the science story.

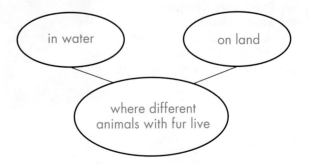

CHAPTER 4 • How to Read Science | **101**

California Science
CONTENT STANDARDS FOCUS

 Life Sciences Students know different plants and animals inhabit different kinds of environments and have external features that help them thrive in different kinds of places.

Objectives

▶ Students tell what an environment is.

▶ Students identify and describe external features that help plants and animals thrive in their environment.

Chapter 4 Lesson 1   30 min

What is an environment?

1. Build Background

Printable Pretest Assess children's background knowledge with Chapter 4 Pretest on *Assessment Book* pp. 41–42.

Science Song Listen to the song "Environments." Have children describe what they see in the large picture on pp. 102–103. Ask children to name other animals that might live in this environment.

Standards Warm Up

Activate Prior Knowledge Ask children to think of different plants and animals they have seen. Discuss with children where these plants and animals lived.

2. Teach

⇒ *QUICK* Plan

▶ As a class, take a picture walk through the lesson to discuss visuals and captions.

▶ **AudioText** Use the audio version of the Student Edition at a technology center.

▶ Encourage children to work in teams to answer lesson questions.

Science Study Notebook
Printable Chapter Study Guide
Have children check their understanding of Chapter 4 by completing pp. 43–44 as they read.

You Are There

Environments
Sung to the tune of "Mary Had A Little Lamb"
Lyrics by Gerri Brioso & Richard Freitas/The Dovetail Group, Inc.

A forest is an environment
With big tall trees
And lots of plants.
A forest is an environment
For different animals.

102

Big Idea	Teacher Background
External features help plants and animals live in their environments.	▶ Animals and plants have external features that help them get food, water, and air in their environments. ▶ The hooves of desert bighorn sheep are sharp and cleaved, or split, which helps them grip the rocks when climbing. The sheep also use their hooves and big horns to take the spines off cacti, which they like to eat. These are examples of adaptations that help an animal live in its environment. ▶ Desert bighorn sheep are an endangered species. Bacteria spread from domestic sheep and the increased predation from mountain lions threaten the survival of the species.

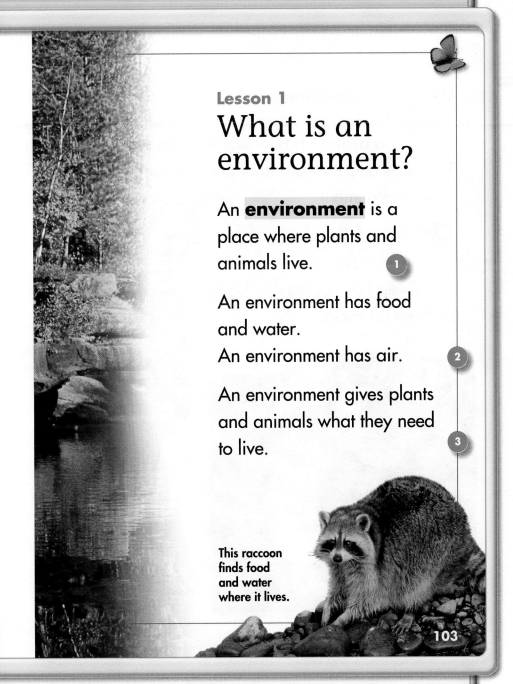

Lesson 1

What is an environment?

An **environment** is a place where plants and animals live. ①

An environment has food and water.
An environment has air. ②

An environment gives plants and animals what they need to live. ③

This raccoon finds food and water where it lives.

103

Universal Access

English Learners
Describe an Environment Examine the large picture on pp. 102–103 and review with children the song "Environments." Ask children to name some things they see in the picture. Discuss how each is part of the environment.

RB9 **ELD Reading**
Beginning Encourage children to draw and label their own pictures of a forest environment. Have volunteers share and describe their drawings.

W1 **ELD Writing**
Intermediate Help children write two sentences about the mountain lion in the picture on pp. 102–103. Have children tell how the lion gets food or water in the environment (for example, "The lion goes down to the water to drink.").

LSA1 **ELD Listening and Speaking**
Advanced Have each child draw a picture of a plant or animal to add to the picture of the forest. Let volunteers explain how it would get what it needs in the environment.

English-Language Arts Support
1RC2.4 **Reading Comprehension**

▶ Read p. 103 aloud with children. Have children look for picture and context clues to help them understand what an environment is.

▶ **Printable Graphic Organizer** Use *Graphic Organizer 1* (TE p. EMxix) with children to help them understand what an environment is. Add as many circles as needed. Children who need extra support can use the completed graphic organizer as a study aid as they complete the lesson.

Scaffolded Questions

Use the following guiding questions to monitor children's comprehension.

① **Recall** What lives in an environment? Plants and animals live in an environment.

② **Restate** What does the environment provide for plants and animals? It provides food, air, and water.

③ **Examine** Why is water an important part of an environment? Plants and animals need water to live.

Extend Science Vocabulary

▶ Write the word **environment** on the board.

▶ Explain that in science, *environment* means "a place where plants and animals live," but in common usage, it can simply mean "surroundings." For example, the classroom is the environment in which children learn.

▶ Ask children to describe things that are part of the classroom environment that help them learn.

▶ **Active Glossary** Children who need more practice with vocabulary terms may review vocabulary online or use vocabulary cards (*Science Study Notebook*, pp. 45–46).

Diagnostic Check

If . . . children have difficulty understanding what an environment is,

then . . . ask children to name various plants and animals. Allow children to name plants and animals that may live in their home or yard. Write the names on the board and have children suggest where each plant and animal might live (in water, in a forest, in a city, in their home). Then review with children plants and animals living in the forest environment on pp. 102–103.

Science Study Notebook

Printable Lesson Study Guide
Have children check their understanding of Lesson 1 by completing p. 50 as they read.

Share and Talk

Ask volunteers to read aloud pp. 104–105. Have children point to the parts of the plants and animals in the pictures they read about. Discuss with children how the split hooves of the desert bighorn sheep help it when climbing rocks and how the giraffe's long neck helps it live where there are leaves high in the trees for food. Tell children how the color of some animals can make them hard to see and can protect them from other animals. Encourage children to think of other external features of plants or animals that help them live in their environments.

Ask: How might the brown and yellow color of the giraffe help it to live in its environment? *The color of the giraffe might make it hard to see and hide it from other animals.*

Write About Science

1WS1.2 Writing Strategies Ask children to write two sentences that describe an animal living in an environment. Tell children to use as many descriptive words as they can to tell about the animal's environment.

Writing Rubric

4	The child's sentences are exceptionally clear and focused. The child vividly describes an animal and its environment. There are few errors.
3	The child's sentences are clear and focused. The child sufficiently describes an animal and its environment. There are some errors.
2	The child's sentences stay on topic. The child includes minimal details about an animal and its environment. There are many errors.
1	The child's sentences are incomplete and lack focus. The writing has few or no details about an animal and its environment. There are many errors that make comprehension difficult.

Tip

Assist children who struggle to organize their ideas by helping them make a list of things in their animal's environment. Explain to children that they can refer to their list as they write.

Living in an Environment

Plants and animals have parts you can see. The parts help plants and animals to live in their environment.

1 *Clip Clop!* This sheep lives where it is rocky. The sheep has hooves to climb on rocks.

2 This plant does not get much sunlight. It has big leaves that take in more of the sunlight it gets.

Hooves

104

Universal Access

Special Needs
Sounds from Different Environments Have children with visual impairments listen to a recording of sounds from different environments. Ask children to identify where they might hear the different sounds on the recording. Then talk with children about what animals and plants live in those environments.

Advanced Learners
Research Local Animals Have children observe animals they can see from their home or the school. Have children choose one animal and research it in the library media center. Ask children to draw a picture of the animal's environment and write two sentences to explain how the animal gets food and water in its environment.

Giraffes have long necks. Giraffes can reach the leaves high in a tree.

Long necks help giraffes see animals that may hurt them too.

Crunch!

See the giraffe eat leaves.

✓ **Lesson Review**

1. What is an environment?
   1. An environment is a place where plants and animals live.

TARGET SKILL

2. **Use Context Clues** What body part helps a giraffe reach leaves in trees? Look for clues in the picture.
   2. A giraffe's long neck helps it reach leaves in trees.

105

Universal Access

Extra Support
Make a Table Copy the table below on the board. Read aloud the headings *Animal* and *Part*. Tell children that all living things have features or parts that help them live in their environment. Review with children that desert bighorn sheep have hooves that help them climb on rocks, and giraffes have long necks that help them reach leaves in tall trees. Invite children to think of features that help cats and dogs live in their environment. Ask, "What helps a cat see in the dark? What helps a dog chew a bone?" Add children's responses to the table.

Animal	Part
Desert bighorn	Hooves
Giraffe	Long neck
Cat	
Dog	

Use the following guiding questions to monitor children's comprehension.

1 Restate Where does the sheep in the picture live? The sheep lives where it is rocky.

2 Explain What helps the plant on p. 104 live where there is little sunlight? The plant has big leaves to help it take in more of the sunlight it gets.

3 Evaluate Why might giraffe hooves be different from the hooves of the sheep? Possible answer: Giraffes do not live where it is rocky.

Extend Science Vocabulary

▶ Ask a volunteer to write *rock* on the board. Explain that *rocky* refers to a place with lots of rocks, such as a rugged trail or path.

▶ Explain to children that we use *rocky* as an adjective that describes part of an environment.

▶ Ask children to think of other words to describe something that is rocky (*hard, sharp, crumbly, loose,* and so on).

3. Summarize and Assess

QUICK Summary

▶ The place where plants and animals live is their environment.

▶ Living things get what they need to live from their environment.

▶ The parts of plants and animals you can see help them live in their environment.

Assess
Printable Resources

Lesson Quiz Check for understanding by reviewing children's responses to *Assessment Book* p. 43 or to the Lesson Review in the Student Edition.

Intervention Study Guide Use pp. 28–29 to review and reinforce lesson concepts as needed.

1LS2.a **Life Sciences** Students know different plants and animals inhabit different kinds of environments and have external features that help them thrive in different kinds of places.

Objectives

▶ Students tell what a forest is.

▶ Students identify and describe external features that help plants and animals thrive in a forest environment.

Chapter 4   Lesson 2   ◗ 30 min

What lives in a forest?

1. Build Background

Standards Warm Up

Activate Prior Knowledge Ask children to describe different trees and plants they see around them each day. Ask them to think of a place where there are many of these plants and trees together. What does it look like? What kind of animals do you think live there?

2. Teach

⇒ *QUICK* Plan

▶ As a class, take a picture walk through the lesson to discuss visuals and captions.

▶ **AudioText** Use the audio version of the Student Edition at a technology center.

▶ Encourage children to work in teams to answer lesson questions.

Science Study Notebook

Printable Lesson Study Guide
Have children check their understanding of Lesson 2 by completing p. 51 as they read.

Lesson 2

What lives in a forest?

A forest is an environment.

1 A **forest** has many trees and other plants. Some forests get cold in winter.

This plant grows in a forest.

106

Big Ideas	Teacher Background
A forest is an environment with many trees and plants.	▶ Deciduous and coniferous forests are found in places that have a cool winter season. Deciduous trees lose their leaves in the winter. Coniferous trees have needlelike leaves and spread their seeds through cones. Most conifers are evergreens.
	▶ Tropical rain forests are found in climates with high annual rainfall and also in areas around the equator. There is no winter season in which the vegetation loses leaves.
Animals have features that help them thrive in their environment.	▶ Black bears have long, curved claws on each foot. The claws help the bears to dig for rodents, insects, and plant tubers to eat.
	▶ Woodpeckers have strong, chisel-like bills for pecking holes. The acorn woodpecker, which is common in California oak forests, drills holes in trees for storing acorns. A single tree can have up to 50,000 holes.

Trees have different kinds of leaves.
Some trees have flat leaves.
Some trees have leaves that
look like needles.

The pine tree keeps its needle leaves in the winter. The waxy needles help the pine tree hold water during the winter.

2
3

1. ✓Checkpoint What is a forest?
1. A forest is an environment that has many trees and other plants.

2. **Use Context Clues** What property of pine tree leaves help the tree live in winter?
2. Possible answer: The waxy needles help the pine tree hold water during winter.

TARGET SKILL

107

Universal Access

English Learners
Describe Features of Forest Animals Examine the pictures of the bears and the woodpecker. Read pp. 108–109 aloud. Talk with children about the features of the black bear and the woodpecker that help them thrive in their environment.

LSB3 ELD Listening and Speaking
Beginning On the board, write *sharp claws, thick fur, sharp bill*. Read the phrases aloud. Have children point to pictures and use the words in sentences: *The ___ has ___*.

WE3 ELD Writing
Intermediate Have children work in pairs to write about the bears and the woodpecker. Provide sentence stems such as *The bear has ___. The woodpecker has ___*. Have children take turns reading their sentences aloud.

LSA4 ELD Listening and Speaking
Advanced Have children draw a picture of a black bear and label its sharp claws and thick fur. Then have children describe their bear to a partner. Encourage children to tell how the bear's features help it live.

English-Language Arts Support

1RW1.1 Word Analysis, Fluency, and Systematic Vocabulary Development

Read pp. 106–107 aloud to children. Write the word *forest* on the board and have children point to it in the heading "What lives in a forest?" Model how to read the heading as a question. Then have children read it aloud with you. Explain that another word for *forest* is *woods*. Write this sentence on the board and have children read it with you: "What lives in the woods?"

Scaffolded Questions

Use the following guiding questions to monitor children's comprehension.

1 **Tell** Which environment has many trees and plants? A forest has many trees and other plants.

2 **Interpret** Why do pine trees keep their needles during the winter? The needles help the pine tree hold water.

3 **Analyze** If the pine tree didn't have needles, what might happen to it during the winter? It wouldn't have the water it needs to live.

Extend Science Vocabulary

▶ Gather pictures of **forests** to show the class. You can find forest pictures in books, magazines, and on the Internet. If possible, include pictures of rain forests, deciduous forests, and coniferous forests.

▶ Discuss with children what they see in common in the pictures. Help them define the critical attributes of a forest.

▶ DIGITAL **9** **Active Glossary** Children who need more practice with vocabulary terms may review vocabulary online or use vocabulary cards (*Science Study Notebook*, pp. 45–46).

Diagnostic Check

If . . . children have difficulty understanding what a forest is,

then . . . have children examine pictures of a forest and pictures of an environment with few trees. Ask children to name some differences they see between an environment with few trees and a forest.

Share and Talk

Ask volunteers to read aloud pp. 108–109. Review with children the features that help the bear and the woodpecker survive in the forest.

Ask: Why do you think woodpeckers and other animals prepare for the winter? Possible answer: There is less food in the forest in the winter, which makes it harder for some animals to find food.

Write About Science

1WA2.2 Writing Applications Ask children to write two sentences from the point of view of a bear that tell how the bear uses its sharp claws, thick fur, or other external features to live in the forest. Tell children to include as many details as they can in their sentences.

Writing Rubric

4	The child's sentences are exceptionally clear and focused. The child vividly describes how the bear uses its features. There are few errors.
3	The child's sentences are clear and focused. The child sufficiently describes how the bear uses its features. There are some errors.
2	The child's sentences stay on topic. The child includes minimal details about how the bear uses its features. There are many errors.
1	The child's sentences are incomplete. The writing has few or no details about how the bear uses its features. There are many errors that make comprehension difficult.

Tip
Have children draw a picture of a bear. Ask them to explain the features they drew. Then help children write their sentences.

Animals Living in Forests

Many animals live in forests.
Black bears live in forests.
Black bears have sharp claws.
Black bears can use their claws
to climb trees and to get food.

Scratch!

This baby bear has sharp claws.

108

Universal Access

Special Needs
Examine Tree Leaves For children with visual impairments, bring in pine needles and some varieties of flat leaves that they can feel and examine. Talk about how pine needles hold water and help pine trees live in cold weather.

Advanced Learners
Research Rain Forest Plants and Animals Have children research the kinds of trees and animals that live in a rain forest. Have children make a diorama of a rain forest, making sure to include at least two types of plants and two types of animals. Research can be done at the library media center using books such as *The Great Kapok Tree: A Tale of the Amazon Rain Forest*, by Lynne Cherry (ISBN: 0-15-202614-2).

Black bears have thick fur too. The fur keeps black bears warm in the forest.

Rat-a-tat-tat!

This woodpecker uses its bill to make holes in trees. The woodpecker puts acorns in the holes to eat in winter. ③

✓ Lesson Review

1. What body parts does a black bear have that help it live in a forest?

   1. A black bear has sharp claws and thick fur that help it live in a forest.

2. ✎ **Writing in Science** Describe how a woodpecker uses its bill to live in a forest.

   2. Possible answer: The woodpecker uses its bill to make holes in trees. It puts acorns in the holes to eat in winter.

109

Universal Access

Extra Support

Dress for Cold Environments Help children understand that people can do things that help them live in different environments. Discuss what things people do that help them live in cold environments. (They wear warmer clothing, such as coats, jackets, hats, and gloves.) You may want to have children draw a picture of a winter scene that shows people dressed in winter clothing. Orthopedically challenged children who are comfortable with assessing their condition might understand that objects that help them move, such as wheelchairs and braces, are things that help them live in their environment.

Use the following guiding questions to monitor children's comprehension.

1. **Repeat** For what can black bears use their claws? Black bears can use their claws to climb trees and get food.

2. **Explain** How does the fur of the black bear help it live in the forest? The bear's fur keeps it warm in the forest.

3. **Analyze** Why do you think woodpeckers store acorns in trees for the winter? Possible answer: The woodpeckers need to save food for the winter because there is less food when it is cold.

Extend Science Vocabulary

▶ Write the word *bill* on the board.

▶ Explain that *bill* is a word that has several different meanings (paper money, a printed ad or notice, the program for a theater performance). Point out that in this lesson *bill* means "a bird's beak."

▶ Have children point to the woodpecker's bill on p. 109. Ask volunteers to use the word *bill* in a sentence about the bird.

3. Summarize and Assess

⇒ *QUICK* Summary

▶ A forest is an environment that has many different kinds of trees and other plants.

▶ Trees have different kinds of leaves: some are flat, and some are needlelike.

▶ Many different animals live in forests.

▶ Black bears have sharp claws and thick fur that help them survive in the forest.

Assess

📀 **Printable Resources**

Lesson Quiz Check for understanding by reviewing children's responses to *Assessment Book* p. 44 or to the Lesson Review in the Student Edition.

Intervention Study Guide Use pp. 30–31 to review and reinforce lesson concepts as needed.

1LS2.a Life Sciences Students know different plants and animals inhabit different kinds of environments and have external features that help them thrive in different kinds of places.

Objectives

▶ Students tell what an ocean is.

▶ Students identify and describe external features that help plants and animals thrive in an ocean environment.

Chapter 4   Lesson 3   30 min

What lives in an ocean?

1. Build Background

Standards Warm Up

Activate Prior Knowledge Show children a globe or world map. Have a volunteer point to an ocean. Ask children what they think lives in the ocean. Write their responses on the board, and review them after you have completed the lesson.

2. Teach

⮞ QUICK Plan

▶ As a class, take a picture walk through the lesson to discuss visuals and captions.

▶ **AudioText** Use the audio version of the Student Edition at a technology center.

▶ Encourage children to work in teams to answer lesson questions.

Science Study Notebook

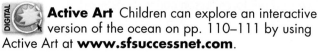

Printable Lesson Study Guide
Have children check their understanding of Lesson 3 by completing p. 52 as they read.

Share and Talk

Read pp. 110–111 aloud. Discuss how the plants' and animals' features help them survive in the ocean.

Active Art Children can explore an interactive version of the ocean on pp. 110–111 by using Active Art at **www.sfsuccessnet.com**.

Lesson 3

What lives in an ocean?

An ocean is an environment.
An **ocean** is a large body of salt water.
Many animals and plants live in an ocean.
 Some parts of an ocean are deep.

 Look for Active Art animations at www.sfsuccessnet.com

This kelp plant has round floats. Floats lift the plant up to the surface. The plant can get the sunlight it needs.

This sea urchin has sharp spines. The spines protect it from other animals in the ocean. **2**

110

Big Ideas	**Teacher Background**
An ocean is a large body of salt water where many plants and animals live.	▶ All of the oceans are connected in a large, continuous body of salt water. Oceans and seas cover almost three-fourths of Earth's surface. ▶ Oceans support life that ranges from the smallest plankton to large sea mammals, such as whales and dolphins. **Common Misconception** Children might believe that only fish and plants live in the ocean. Mammals also live in the ocean.
Sea animals have features that help them survive.	▶ Most fish use gills to breathe. Tiny blood vessels in the gills absorb oxygen directly from the water. ▶ Sea mammals, such as whales, have lungs and must come to the surface regularly to breathe in oxygen from the air.

Gulp!
This fish lives in the ocean. The fish has gills to breathe in water. 3

Gill

1. ✓Checkpoint What is an ocean?
   1. An ocean has salt water and is big.
2. What helps a kelp plant get sunlight in an ocean?
   2. Floats help a kelp plant get sunlight in an ocean.

DIGITAL NSTA SciLinks
keyword: **ocean**
code: **gr1p110**

111

Universal Access

English Learners
Life in the Ocean Examine the pictures on pp. 110–113 and read the captions with the children. Make a bulletin board titled "Ocean." Ask children what should go on the bulletin board.

LSB3 Listening and Speaking
Beginning Have children draw a picture of a plant or animal that lives in the ocean. Help children write labels for their drawing and read them. Post drawings on the board.

W14 ELD Writing
Intermediate Ask pairs of children to name words that describe an ocean environment. Have them use the words to complete this sentence: *The ocean is ___.* Post sentences on the board.

WA4 ELD Writing
Advanced Ask children to choose a plant or animal that lives in the ocean. Help children write sentences about how the external features help the plant or animal live in the ocean.

Mathematics Support
1MG2.4 Measurement and Geometry

▶ Examine the picture on p. 111 as a class. Ask children to choose one fish in the picture.

▶ Have children find and label other fish in the picture. Ask children to describe the position of the other fish in relation to their chosen fish using terms such as *near, far, below, above, up, down, behind, in front of, next to, left of* or *right of*. Make sure children understand these terms before beginning the activity.

Scaffolded Questions

Use the following guiding questions to monitor children's comprehension.

1 **Name** Name two things about an ocean. Possible answers: It has salt water; it is big; it is home to many plants and animals.

2 **Describe** What protects a sea urchin from other animals? The sea urchin has sharp spines that protect it from other animals.

3 **Propose** How does the fish breathe the air it needs to live? The fish has gills to breathe in the water.

Extend Science Vocabulary

▶ Write the word **ocean** on the board.

▶ Ask children to say some words that are used to describe an ocean. Write them under the word.

▶ Ask children to add words they learn as they complete the lesson.

▶ DIGITAL 9 **Active Glossary** Children who need more practice with vocabulary terms may review vocabulary online or use vocabulary cards (*Science Study Notebook*, pp. 45–46).

▶ DIGITAL SciLinks **SciLinks** Children can go online to discover more about the *ocean* by using the NSTA *SciLink* available at **www.sfsuccessnet.com** (keyword: **ocean** code: **gr1p110**).

Diagnostic Check

If . . . children have trouble understanding that an ocean is an environment,

then . . . show them pictures of ocean and land environments. Ask them to identify the plants and animals in the pictures. Discuss that both land and ocean environments have plants and animals that get what they need from their surroundings.

2. Teach CONTINUED

Share and Talk

Read p. 112 to children. Help volunteers read captions on pp. 112–113 aloud. Tell children that animals such as sea otters and albatross drink sea water and eat sea animals. Discuss some features that help animals live in an ocean environment.

Ask: What do you think ocean animals eat? Possible answer: Ocean animals probably eat other ocean animals and plants.

Write About Science

1WS1.1 **Writing Strategies** Ask children to write two sentences about a sea animal. Have them choose one animal from the lesson: the sea otter, the gray whale, or the albatross.

Writing Rubric

4	The child's sentences are exceptionally clear and are focused on one sea animal. The child includes interesting details about the animal. There are few or no errors.
3	The child's sentences are clear and are focused on one sea animal. The child includes some details about the animal. There are some errors.
2	The child's sentences are difficult to follow. The child includes few details about the animal. There are many errors.
1	The child's sentences are incomplete. The child includes no details about the animal. There are many errors.

Tip

Have children list some details about the animal they chose. Help children to form sentences about their animal using these details.

Other Animals in an Ocean Environment

2 ***Splish splash!*** Look at the sea otter! Thick fur keeps the sea otter warm. A sea otter drinks salt water. A sea otter finds food in the ocean too.

A sea otter can rest by floating on its back.

112

Universal Access

Special Needs

How Ocean Animals Move Ask children to act out how different animals might move in the ocean. They can imitate the animals shown on pp. 110–113, or they can make up their own movements.

Advanced Learners

Research Endangered Species Explain to children that sea otters and many whales appear on the endangered species list. Have children select another endangered sea animal using resources at the library media center, such as the list provided at the U.S. Fish and Wildlife Service's Web site at http://www.fws.gov. Ask children to research the animal's external features, its environment, and the reasons the animal is endangered. Encourage them to orally share what they learned about the animal.

112 UNIT B • Life Sciences

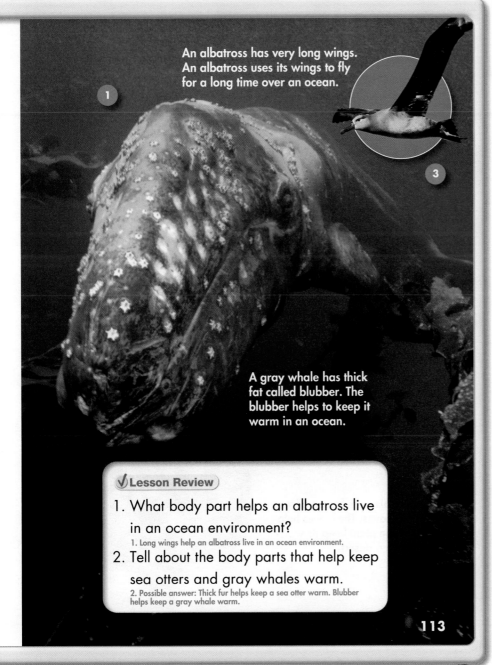

An albatross has very long wings. An albatross uses its wings to fly for a long time over an ocean.

A gray whale has thick fat called blubber. The blubber helps to keep it warm in an ocean.

✔ Lesson Review

1. What body part helps an albatross live in an ocean environment?

   1. Long wings help an albatross live in an ocean environment.

2. Tell about the body parts that help keep sea otters and gray whales warm.

   2. Possible answer: Thick fur helps keep a sea otter warm. Blubber helps keep a gray whale warm.

113

Universal Access

Extra Support

Examine Pictures of Sea Animals Ask each child to draw one of the following on a large card: kelp, sea urchin, fish, sea otter, whale, or albatross. Make up statements about the plants and the animals and ask children to hold up their card if the statement is true about the plant or animal they drew. Use statements such as "I live in the ocean" and "I can float on my back."

Use the following guiding questions to monitor children's comprehension.

1 **Name** Name an animal that lives in the ocean. Possible answers: Sea otter, whale, fish

2 **Compare** What do the sea otter in the ocean and the black bear in the forest have in common? Possible answer: They both have thick fur that keeps them warm.

3 **Infer** What does a bird have on its body to keep it warm? A bird has feathers to keep it warm.

Extend Science Vocabulary

▶ Write the word *whale* on the board.

▶ Discuss with children that although a whale is an animal, the word is sometimes used to describe something large. ("It was as big as a whale.") Talk with children about why the word *whale* is associated with large things.

▶ Ask children for other examples of animals that are used to describe something. Get them started by writing "as big as a whale" and "as quiet as a mouse" on the board.

3. Summarize and Assess

▷ *QUICK* Summary

▶ An ocean is an environment that is big and has salt water.

▶ Many sea animals and plants have parts that help them live in the ocean.

▶ Otters and whales have external features that keep them warm in the ocean.

Assess
 Printable Resources

Lesson Quiz Check for understanding by reviewing children's responses to *Assessment Book* p. 45 or to the Lesson Review in the Student Edition.

Intervention Study Guide Use pp. 32–33 to review and reinforce lesson concepts as needed.

Life Sciences Students know different plants and animals inhabit different kinds of environments and have external features that help them thrive in different kinds of places.

Objectives

▶ Students tell what a desert is.

▶ Students identify and describe external features that help plants and animals thrive in a desert environment.

Chapter 4 Lesson 4   30 min

What lives in a desert?

1. Build Background

Standards Warm Up

Activate Prior Knowledge Show children a picture of a desert. Ask children to describe what they see (bright sunlight, rocks, sand, cacti). Then ask volunteers to share what they already know about deserts.

2. Teach

⟫ QUICK Plan

▶ As a class, take a picture walk through the lesson to discuss visuals and captions.

▶ **AudioText** Use the audio version of the Student Edition at a technology center.

▶ Encourage children to work in teams to answer lesson questions.

Science Study Notebook

 **Printable Lesson Study Guide**
Have children check their understanding of Lesson 4 by completing p. 53 as they read.

Lesson 4

What lives in a desert?

A desert is an environment.
A **desert** is very dry.
Many plants and animals live in the desert.

1 A desert gets lots of sunlight.
2 A desert gets very little rain.
Deserts may get hot during the day.

This bush has small waxy leaves. The leaves help the plant keep its water in a desert.

114

Big Ideas	**Teacher Background**
A desert is a dry environment that gets very little rain.	▶ Death Valley in California is an example of a desert. It is one of the hottest places in the world. In the summer, temperatures in Death Valley exceed 38°C (100°F). Rainfall averages less than 2 inches per year.
	Common Misconception Children might think that deserts are hot all of the time. Desert temperatures fluctuate from day to night. In winter, nighttime temperatures in Death Valley can range from 4°C to 9°C (40°F to 49°F).
Desert plants and animals have external features that help them survive.	▶ The desert iguana is found in the Mojave Desert. Its light-colored skin helps it tolerate extreme heat. The desert iguana sometimes climbs into bushes or kangaroo rat burrows for shade, but will remain active when temperatures are as high as 46°C (115°F).
	▶ Some desert plants drop their leaves during dry periods to save water.

Ouch!

This cactus has sharp spines. The spines protect the cactus from animals that may eat it.

3

1. ✓Checkpoint What is a desert? 1. A desert is an environment that is very dry.

2. What part of the cactus helps protect it from animals? 2. The cactus has sharp spines that protect it from animals.

115

Universal Access

English Learners
Discuss External Features of Animals Invite children to name the animals in the pictures on pp. 116–117. Discuss the features each animal has that help it thrive in the desert environment. Show children pictures of other desert animals, such as camels.

(LSB3) ELD Listening and Speaking
Beginning Point to the iguana on p. 116, model how the name is pronounced in English, and ask how children say this word in their home language. Have them draw and color a picture of the iguana in its environment.

(LSE12) ELD Listening and Speaking
Intermediate Have pairs of children take turns pointing to one of the animals and asking a question about the animal. Have each child's partner answer the question.

(RA6) ELD Reading
Advanced Play a guessing game. Have volunteers take turns describing an animal without naming it, and have children guess the animal being described. For example, "I live in a desert and have a long tail and long legs. I can run fast. What am I?" (A roadrunner)

English-Language Arts Support

(1WOL1-2) Written and Oral English Language Conventions

After reading aloud p. 114, ask children to identify the plural nouns in the two paragraphs and list them on the board (*plants, animals, deserts*). Then, ask each child to write a sentence that uses the singular form of one of the nouns.

Scaffolded Questions

Use the following guiding questions to monitor children's comprehension.

1 **Explain** Explain why a desert is dry. Deserts get lots of sunshine and do not get much rain.

2 **Contrast** Name one difference between an ocean environment and a desert environment. An ocean is made of water while a desert gets very little water.

3 **Infer** Where might birds and other animals go when deserts get hot during the day? Possible answer: Birds and animals might go under plants and rocks or in the ground when deserts get hot during the day.

Extend Science Vocabulary

▶ Review the vocabulary word **desert**. A desert is a dry environment that receives little water. Plants and animals live in the desert.

▶ Write the following cloze sentence on the board: *A desert has _____.*

▶ Ask children to copy the sentence and fill in the blank with a word or phrase that describes a desert.

▶ 🄳🄸🄶🄸🅃🄰🄻 9 **Active Glossary** Children who need more practice with vocabulary terms may review vocabulary online or use vocabulary cards (*Science Study Notebook*, pp. 45–46).

Diagnostic Check

If . . . children have trouble understanding the conditions in a desert,

then . . . show children pictures of different deserts placed next to pictures of forests, so children can see differences in the plants and animals side-by-side.

2. Teach CONTINUED

Share and Talk

Read pp. 116–117 with children. Discuss how the light-colored skin of a desert iguana reflects light and helps it control its body temperature. Review how the roadrunner catches food and how the rabbit senses danger.

Ask: What helps each animal live in the desert? Its body part or feature helps it live.

Write About Science

1WA2.2 Writing Applications Have children write a brief description of one of the desert animals on pp. 116–117.

Writing Rubric

4	The child's description is exceptionally clear and focused. The child uses details to create an interesting description of a desert animal. There are few or no errors.
3	The child's description is clear and focused. The child uses some details to describe a desert animal. There are some errors.
2	The child's description lacks focus. The child includes few details about the desert animal. There are many errors.
1	The child's description is not clear and does not describe a desert animal. The writing has few or no details. There are many errors that make the writing difficult to understand.

Tip

Help children list some features of the animal (what it looks like, what it might feel like, what sounds it might make). Model how to use their lists to write a description of an animal.

Animals in a Desert

A desert iguana has light colored skin.
1 Light colors stay cooler in the hot Sun.
The light skin helps the iguana keep cool.

Look at the color of this desert iguana.

116

Universal Access

Special Needs

Touch the Desert Help children with visual impairments understand the desert environment by placing sand in a bowl and allowing them to feel the texture and dryness. Then, leave sand in the sunlight and allow children to feel the warmth of the sand. A hairbrush can be used to allow children to feel what the needles on a cactus might feel like. If possible, bring in an aloe leaf, which can give children an idea of what a cactus would feel like without its needles.

Advanced Learners

Research Camels Have children use the library media center to research how camels survive in desert environments. Ask children to draw a picture of a camel and label some parts that help camels live in the desert. Ask children to present and explain their drawings.

Zoom!

The roadrunner has long legs. It can run very fast to catch food. **2**

Shhh!

This rabbit has long ears that help keep cool. It can hear other animals when they are near. **3**

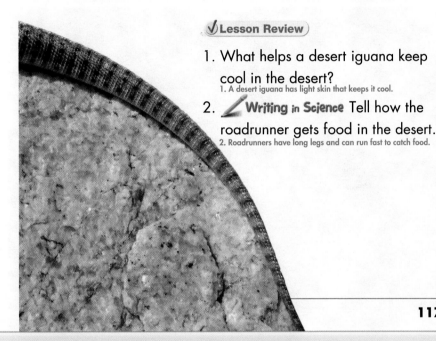

✓ Lesson Review

1. What helps a desert iguana keep cool in the desert?
   1. A desert iguana has light skin that keeps it cool.

2. **Writing** in **Science** Tell how the roadrunner gets food in the desert.
   2. Roadrunners have long legs and can run fast to catch food.

117

Universal Access

Extra Support
Understand How the Iguana Keeps Cool Help children understand how light-colored skin helps iguanas and other desert animals stay cool. Leave a piece of black paper next to a piece of white paper in a sunny spot for an hour or more, and allow children to feel the difference in the temperature.

Use the following guiding questions to monitor children's comprehension.

1 **Recall** What kind of colors stay cooler in the hot Sun? Light colors stay cooler in the hot Sun.

2 **Identify** What animal in the desert has long legs to run fast? The roadrunner has long legs to run fast.

3 **Analyze** Why do you think the rabbit needs long ears to hear other animals when they are near? Possible answer: Rabbits need to hear other animals that may hunt them for food.

Extend Science Vocabulary

▶ Write *iguana, roadrunner,* and *rabbit* on the board.

▶ Have children make a picture vocabulary card for each animal. They should draw the animal on the front and write a descriptive sentence on the back. The sentence should describe external features that help the animal live in the desert.

▶ Have children work in pairs and use their cards to quiz each other about the external features of each animal.

3. Summarize and Assess

⟩ QUICK Summary

▶ A desert environment receives lots of sunlight and very little rain.

▶ Deserts are warm and dry.

▶ Sharp spines protect cacti from animals.

▶ Desert iguanas are light in color to keep them cool.

Assess
Printable Resources

Lesson Quiz Check for understanding by reviewing children's responses to *Assessment Book* p. 46 or to the Lesson Review in the Student Edition.

Intervention Study Guide Use pp. 34–35 to review and reinforce lesson concepts as needed.

1PS1.2 Statistics, Data Analysis, and Probability Represent and compare data (e.g., largest, smallest, most often, least often) by using pictures, bar graphs, tally charts, and picture graphs.

1IE4.c Investigation and Experimentation Record observations on a bar graph.

Objective Students use a bar graph to represent and compare the number of animals in different environments.

Math in Science

 25 min

1. Build Background

Warm Up
Activate Prior Knowledge

▶ Invite children to talk about some different kinds of charts or graphs they have seen, such as a bar graph or picture graph.

▶ Draw some of these on the board. Solicit that bar graphs use bars to show and compare amounts.

2. Teach

Count and Graph

To help children understand bar graphs, have them count the number of boys and girls in the classroom. Then make a bar graph that represents this data.

Ask: What does the bar labeled *girls* show? It shows the number of girls in the classroom. What does the bar labeled *boys* show? It shows the number of boys in the classroom.

Invite children to explain how they could compare the length of the bars on the graph to determine if there are more boys or girls in the class.

Share and Talk

Have children work in pairs to answer the questions on p. 119. Encourage them to discuss how they found the total number of forest animals and the total number of desert animals.

eTools Use the Spreadsheet/Data/Grapher Tools to generate several simple bar graphs. Then ask children to compare data in the graphs.

Math in Science

Comparing Animals

118

show how many animals are in each picture.

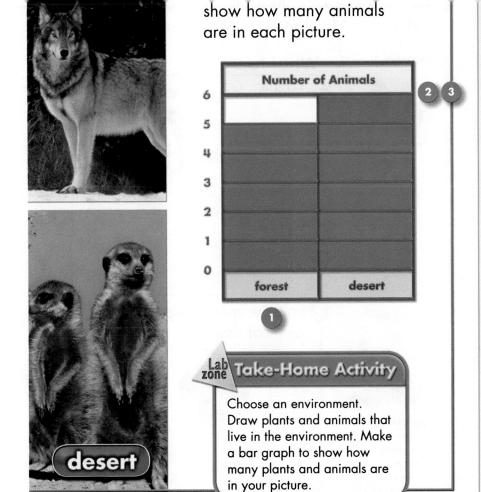

Number of Animals

	forest	desert
6		
5		
4		
3		
2		
1		
0		

desert

Lab zone Take-Home Activity

Choose an environment. Draw plants and animals that live in the environment. Make a bar graph to show how many plants and animals are in your picture.

119

Take-Home Activity

Tips for Success
▶ Encourage children not to draw too many plants or animals in their pictures, as this will make it difficult for them to make an accurate bar graph.

▶ Remind children to label the bars of their graphs.

▶ For children who struggle, discuss the vertical axis of a bar graph. Model how to trace the top of the bar to the number on the axis.

Scaffolded Questions

Use the following guiding questions to monitor children's comprehension.

1 Name What does the bar on the left side of the graph represent? It represents how many animals live in the forest.

2 Explain How can you tell that more animals live in the desert than in the forest? The bar for desert goes up to the number 6, while the bar for forest only goes up to the number 5.

3 Analyze How can you compare amounts on a bar graph without reading the actual numbers on the graph? You can look to see which bar rises higher.

3. Summarize and Assess

QUICK Summary

▶ Bar graphs can be used to represent data.

▶ Bar graphs are useful for comparing numbers.

▶ You can use bar graphs to record observations.

Assess

Check for understanding by reviewing responses to questions on p. 119. Children may explain that they counted the number of animals in each environment and then filled in the bar graph.

Objective Students use a model to explain how the leaves of a desert plant help it live in the desert.

Guided Inquiry ⏱ **20 min**

1. Get Ready

Materials for Small Groups

desert leaf shapes
(Activity Master 1)

green construction paper

spray bottle

water

waxed paper

plate or tray (optional)

Materials listed in *italics* are kit materials.

Alternative Materials Children can use moistened paper towels to wet the leaves. If a sunny place is not available, place the leaves under a lamp with a 40 watt bulb.

⇒ QUICK Plan

▶ This activity may be set up as a center activity.

2. What to Do

Preview

▶ 🔵 **Active Glossary** Reinforce science vocabulary by encouraging children to use academic language from the chapter as they do the activity. For children who need extra support, post vocabulary cards (*Science Study Notebook*, pp. 45–46).

▶ Conduct an inventory of materials with children. For English Learners, solicit alternative names for items in their home language. Post the names of materials and other academic language, such as *observe*.

▶ You may wish to preview science content in Lesson 4.

Advance Preparation

▶ Cut waxed paper into 12 x 12 in. squares.

▶ Copy Activity Master 1 (*Science Study Notebook Teacher's Guide* p. T58) onto green construction paper and cut out two paper leaves for each group.

▶ Fill the spray bottle with water.

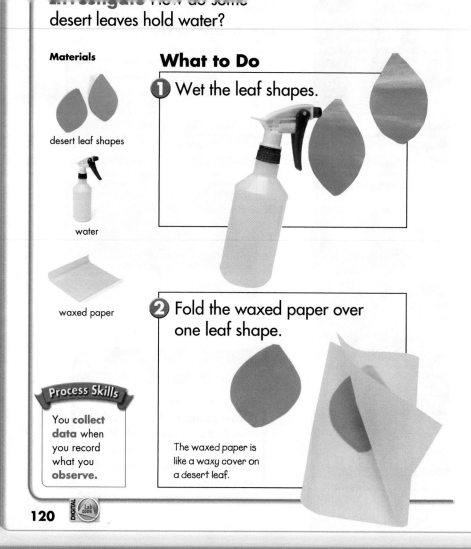

desert leaves hold water?

Materials

desert leaf shapes

water

waxed paper

Process Skills

You **collect data** when you record what you **observe.**

What to Do

1 Wet the leaf shapes.

2 Fold the waxed paper over one leaf shape.

The waxed paper is like a waxy cover on a desert leaf.

120

Digital Classroom

🎬 **Activity Video** Prepare for and rehearse the activity before class.

🖨 **Printable Activity Rubric** Monitor children's progress using the Activity Rubric located at **www.sfsuccessnet.com**.

🔬 **Printable LabZone Activity** Provide children with additional activities located at **www.sfsuccessnet.com**.

Call **1-888-537-4908** with activity questions.

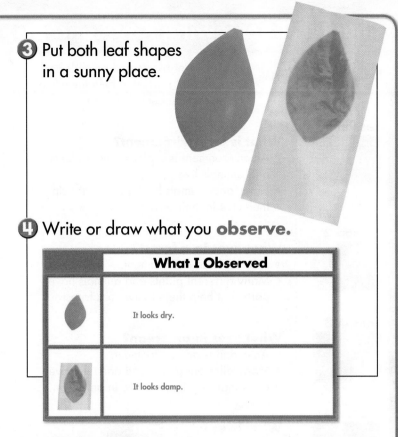

3 Put both leaf shapes in a sunny place.

4 Write or draw what you **observe.**

What I Observed	
	It looks dry.
	It looks damp.

Explain Your Results

1. Which holds water longer? Leaf with waxed paper

2. **Interpret data.** How do waxy leaves help desert plants? Waxy leaves help a plant keep the water it needs.

Go Further

What might happen if the leaves were put in a dark place? Plan a test to find out.

121

Big Idea

Desert plants have features that help them survive in a dry habitat.

Teacher Background

▶ Plants and animals have external features that help them thrive in their environments. In a hot, dry climate, water is scarce and evaporates quickly, so desert plants have adaptations that help them store water.

▶ Many desert plants, such as cactuses, aloe, and agave, have a waxy cuticle that is nearly waterproof.

Tips

▶ Make sure children wet both leaves evenly.

▶ Have children fold wax paper over one leaf shape to resemble the waxy covering of a desert leaf.

Record Data Tell children that a chart should present data clearly. Each column should have a heading that tells what is in the column. Each row should have a picture or heading that tells what is in the row. Check the leaf shapes after an hour. Keep them in the sunlight until the uncovered leaf is dry. Then have children compare their two leaves and collect data. Have children write or draw what they observe.

Ask Questions Ask children what they did to each leaf. How did it make the leaves different when they were left in the light?

3. Explain Your Results

Science Study Notebook

Printable Resources Activity Recording Sheet
Discuss the results of the activity by reviewing completed pp. 54–55. Ask volunteers to tell what they observed as the leaves were dried by the light.

Activity Rubric Use *Science Study Notebook Teacher's Guide* p. T27 to evaluate children's work.

Go Further

▶ Discuss what else might affect the water in leaves. What would happen if the leaf shapes were put in a dark place? Ask children how they could design a new experiment to find out.

▶ Ask children for additional questions about leaves and post them on the bulletin board. Encourage children to investigate these questions on their own.

1. Lesson Summaries

▶ Review the lesson summaries on p. 122 by asking children each lesson focus question and encouraging them to answer using their own words. If children struggle to answer, have them look at the lesson pictures to review the concepts.

▶ Divide the class into four groups, and assign each group one lesson from the chapter. Children should review the material in their assigned lesson.

▶ Have each group work together to develop a poster for its assigned lesson. Children may suggest alternate ideas for visually displaying information about where plants and animals live. Encourage groups to label and use captions for all parts of their poster.

2. Reinforce Concepts

▶ Have each group present its lesson poster to the class. Encourage groups to give details that show how the topics in their lesson relate to the chapter's Big Idea. Invite children to discuss the work of other groups.

▶ Suggest to children that they combine their posters to make a mural for the chapter.

▶ When the class mural is complete, children may use it to prepare for the Chapter 4 Review/Test (pp. 124–125).

Chapter 4 Reviewing Key Concepts

 Focus on the BIG Idea Different plants and animals have different parts that help them live in different environments.

Lesson 1

What is an environment?
- An environment is a place where plants and animals live.
- Plants and animals have parts that help them live in their environment.

Lesson 2

What lives in a forest?
- A forest is an environment.
- Many different plants and animals have parts that help them to live in a forest.

Lesson 3

What lives in an ocean?
- An ocean is an environment.
- Many different plants and animals have parts that help them to live in an ocean.

Lesson 4

What lives in a desert?
- A desert is an environment.
- Many different plants and animals have parts that help them to live in a desert.

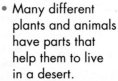

122

Further Learning

Give advanced learners the task of inserting vocabulary words or brief phrases into the mural. These should be added at appropriate places in the mural and should help summarize the key ideas presented in the mural.

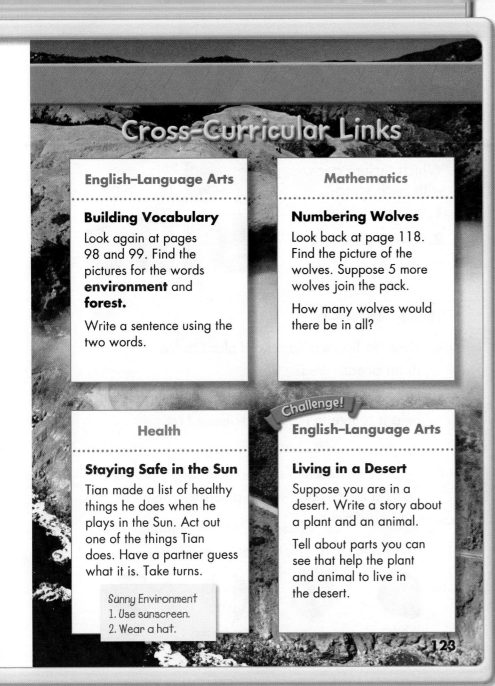

Cross-Curricular Links

English–Language Arts

Building Vocabulary

Look again at pages 98 and 99. Find the pictures for the words **environment** and **forest.**

Write a sentence using the two words.

Mathematics

Numbering Wolves

Look back at page 118. Find the picture of the wolves. Suppose 5 more wolves join the pack.

How many wolves would there be in all?

Health

Staying Safe in the Sun

Tian made a list of healthy things he does when he plays in the Sun. Act out one of the things Tian does. Have a partner guess what it is. Take turns.

Sunny Environment
1. Use sunscreen.
2. Wear a hat.

Challenge! English–Language Arts

Living in a Desert

Suppose you are in a desert. Write a story about a plant and an animal.

Tell about parts you can see that help the plant and animal to live in the desert.

123

3. Chapter Focus Questions

▶ Direct children's attention to the Big Idea on p. 122. Have children give an oral summary about the Big Idea. Encourage children to use vocabulary terms and other academic language from the chapter. Answers will vary.

▶ Make a T-chart with columns labeled *Ocean* and *Forest* for children to use to describe different plants and animals living in an ocean and a forest. Answers will vary.

Ask:

▶ Could forest plants and animals live in a desert environment? No. The desert environment would be too hot and dry for forest plants and animals to live.

Cross-Curricular Links

English-Language Arts
Building Vocabulary

1WOL1.1 **Written and Oral English Language Conventions** Answers will vary. See the Writing Rubric for Building Vocabulary to the right for support on scoring children's writing.

Mathematics
Numbering Wolves

1NS2.1 **Number Sense** 10 wolves

Health
Staying Safe in the Sun

Improvisations will vary.

English-Language Arts
Challenge **Living in a Desert**

1WA2.1 **Writing Applications** Possible answer: I see a cactus. The cactus has spines. The spines protect the cactus from animals. I see a rabbit. The rabbit has long ears. The rabbit can hear other animals that may harm it.

Writing Rubric for Building Vocabulary

4	Child writes a clear, complete sentence that correctly uses both words. Capitalization and punctuation are correct.
3	Child writes a sentence that uses both words correctly. Sentence may have errors in capitalization or end mark.
2	Child writes a sentence that uses only one of the words correctly. Sentence may have errors in both capitalization and end mark.
1	Child writes an unfocused and unclear sentence that has many errors.

Vocabulary

1. B
2. C
3. A

Think About It

4. The floats help lift the kelp plant to get sunlight in an ocean.

5. The desert iguana has light-colored skin. Light colors stay cooler in the hot sun.

6. Possible answer: A black bear has fur to keep it warm in the forest.

7. **Classify** The bear and the woodpecker belong in a forest. The whale and the fish belong in an ocean.

Refer to side columns for answers

Chapter 4 Review/Test

Vocabulary

Which picture goes with each word?

1. forest (page 100)
2. ocean (page 104)
3. desert (page 108)

Think About It

4. How do floats help a kelp plant to live in an ocean? (page 110)

5. How does the skin color of the desert iguana help it to live in the desert? (page 116)

6. **Writing in Science** Tell about a body part that helps a black bear live in a forest. (page 108)

7. **Process Skills** **Classify** Which animals belong in a forest and which in an ocean? (pages 108–113)

Whale   **Bear**   **Woodpecker**   **Fish**

124

Universal Access

Special Needs

Accommodate individual children as needed to distinguish between lack of content knowledge and physical or linguistic limitations.

Common Accommodations

▶ Provide additional time.

▶ **AudioText** Read the test. An audio recording of the Chapter Review/Test is available on AudioText.

▶ Allow children who have difficulty writing to audio record answers.

Assessment Resources

Printable Chapter Test
Assessment Book pp. 47–50

Success Tracker
Use this flexible, online assessment system to track Adequate Yearly Progress and provide intervention. Find it at **www.sfsuccessnet.com**.

Printable Student Progress Report
TE pp. EMxvii–EMxviii

Show What You Know
TE pp. 166–167

ExamView
Customizable Chapter 4 Test

MindPoint QuizShow
Chapter 4 review in game format

8. Use Context Clues

Where does the plant live?

(page 114)

Small waxy leaves help this plant keep water in a desert.

California Standards Practice

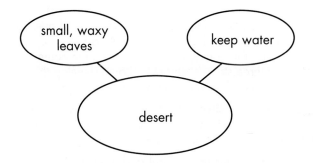

Write the letter of the correct answer.

9. Where do all plants and animals live?

   A in a desert

   B in an ocean

   C in an environment

   D in a forest

10. Look at the picture. What body part helps this sheep live in its environment?

   A feathers to keep it warm.

   B blubber to keep it warm.

   C a long neck to reach leaves

   D hooves to climb on rocks.

125

Use Context Clues

8. Possible answer:

```
   (small, waxy          (keep water)
     leaves)
            \           /
             (desert)
```

California Standards Practice

9. C

10. D

Intervention and Reteaching

California Science CONTENT STANDARDS FOCUS	Review Items	Student Edition	Teacher's Edition Resources				Ancillary Resources	
			Scaffolded Questions	Extend Vocab	Diagnostic Check		Intervention Study Guide	Science Study Notebook
1LS2.a **Life Sciences** Students know different plants and animals inhabit different kinds of environments and have external features that help them thrive in different kinds of places.	1–10	98–121	103, 105, 107, 109, 111, 113, 115, 117	103, 105, 107, 109, 111, 113, 115, 117	103, 107, 111, 115		28–35	43–44, 45–46, 48, 50–53, 54–55

Biography

🕐 25 min

1. Build Background

Warm Up
Activate Prior Knowledge

▶ Have children discuss what they know about scientists.

▶ **Ask:** What are some things scientists do? What kinds of things might scientists study? Note: Children may need some guidance and coaching to arrive at answers. Possible answer: Scientists may study plants, animals, diseases, and other aspects of the natural world. They do so by working in laboratories, in the field, and with other scientists.

▶ Write children's responses in a chart and revisit at the end of the discussion.

2. Teach

Share and Talk

Read p. 126 together. Then have children write a letter to Dr. Sonia Ortega. Encourage children to include questions such as:

▶ What did you learn about oysters?

▶ What kind of work are you doing now?

Have advanced learners include in their letters a list of questions that they think scientists should try to answer.

3. Summarize and Assess

▶ Have children create a word web that describes some of the actions Dr. Ortega has taken as a scientist.

▶ After they have created their word webs, have children list two questions they would like to ask about Dr. Ortega. Possible answers: 1. What kinds of insects did you look for when you were young? 2. What kinds of things did you want to learn about animals?

Dr. Sonia Ortega

Read Together
Dr. Sonia Ortega liked to look for insects when she was young. When she grew up she wanted to learn more about other animals.

Dr. Ortega became a marine biologist. She studied how oysters live in the ocean. She wanted to learn where oysters grow the best.

Dr. Ortega knows that scientists must ask good questions and do careful studies to learn more.

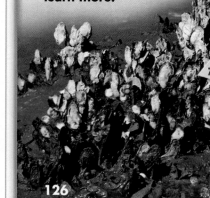

Lab zone **Take-Home Activity**

Look for a place where plants and animals live near your home. Draw a picture of the place.

126

Big Idea	Teacher Background
Good scientists ask good questions and do careful studies.	▶ Scientists use scientific methods to try to answer questions. Scientists make observations to form a hypothesis, which is then tested in an experiment to see if it can be supported. If the experiment does not support it, the hypothesis is revised and tested again.

Common Misconception Scientists do not devise experiments to just "see what they can discover." The studies are carefully planned, and scientists often know what to expect from them.

Take-Home Activity

Tips for Success

▶ Encourage children to show animals, or evidence of animal life, in their drawings.

▶ Have children label their drawings.

Chapter 5

Plants and Animals Living Together

1LS2.0 Plants and animals meet their needs in different ways. As a basis for understanding this concept:

1LS2.a Students know different plants and animals inhabit different kinds of environments and have external features that help them thrive in different kinds of places.

1LS2.c Students know animals eat plants or other animals for food and may also use plants or even other animals for shelter and nesting.

1LS2.d Students know how to infer what animals eat from the shapes of their teeth (e.g., sharp teeth: eats meat; flat teeth: eats plants).

1IE4.0 Scientific progress is made by asking meaningful questions and conducting careful investigations. As a basis for understanding this concept and addressing the content in the other three strands, students should develop their own questions and perform investigations.

1IE4.a Draw pictures that portray some features of the thing being described.

1IE4.b Record observations and data with pictures, numbers, or written statements.

1IE4.c Record observations on a bar graph.

Standards Focus Questions

- How do plants and animals need one another?

- How do animals help spread seeds?

- What is a food chain?

- How do living things get food in a desert?

- How do living things get food in a marsh?

- What do animals eat?

LESSON TITLES AND PACING

California Science CONTENT STANDARDS

Plants and Animals Living Together

Lab zone **Directed Inquiry**

⏱ 10 min

Explore
What do animals eat for food?
p. 130

1LS2.c Students know animals eat plants or other animals for food and may also use plants or even other animals for shelter and nesting.
1IE4.b Record observations and data with pictures, numbers, or written statements.

LESSON 1

How do plants and animals need one another?
pp. 132–135

⏱ 30 min

1LS2.c Students know animals eat plants or other animals for food and may also use plants or even other animals for shelter and nesting.

LESSON 2

How do animals help spread seeds?
pp. 136–137

⏱ 20 min

1LS2.c Students know animals eat plants or other animals for food and may also use plants or even other animals for shelter and nesting.

LESSON 3

What is a food chain?
pp. 138–139

⏱ 20 min

1LS2.c Students know animals eat plants or other animals for food and may also use plants or even other animals for shelter and nesting.

LESSON 4

How do living things get food in a desert?
pp. 140–143

⏱ 30 min

1LS2.c Students know animals eat plants or other animals for food and may also use plants or even other animals for shelter and nesting.

LESSON 5

How do living things get food in a marsh?
pp. 144–147

⏱ 30 min

1LS2.c Students know animals eat plants or other animals for food and may also use plants or even other animals for shelter and nesting.

LESSON 6

What do animals eat?
pp. 148–151

⏱ 30 min

1LS2.d Students know how to infer what animals eat from the shape of their teeth (e.g., sharp teeth: eats meat; flat teeth: eats plants).

Lab zone **Guided Inquiry**

⏱ 20 min

Investigate
How can you make a model of a food chain?
pp. 154–155

1LS2.c Students know animals eat plants or other animals for food and may also use plants or even other animals for shelter and nesting.
1IE4.a Draw pictures that portray some features of the thing being described.
1IE4.b Record observations and data with pictures, numbers, or written statements.

Reviewing Key Concepts

⏱ 25 min

Review and assess each science content standard from the chapter as listed above.

Chapter 5 Review/Test
pp. 156–159

Lab zone **Full Inquiry**

⏱ 20 min

Experiment
How can color help mice stay hidden from hawks?
pp. 164–165

1LS2.a Students know different plants and animals inhabit different kinds of environments and have external features that help them thrive in different kinds of places.
1IE4.c Record observations on a bar graph.

VOCAB/SKILLS	ASSESSMENT/INTERVENTION
Process Skill: Infer	• **Explain Your Results,** SE p. 130 • **Activity Recording Sheet,** *Science Study Notebook* p. 62 • **Activity Rubric,** *Science Study Notebook Teacher's Guide* p. T28
shelter	• **Scaffolded Questions,** TE pp. 133, 135 • **Chapter Study Guide,** *Science Study Notebook* pp. 57–58 • **Lesson Study Guide,** *Science Study Notebook* p. 64 • **Lesson Quiz,** *Assessment Book* p. 53
	• **Scaffolded Questions,** TE p. 136 • **Lesson Study Guide,** *Science Study Notebook* p. 65 • **Lesson Quiz,** *Assessment Book* p. 54
food chain	• **Scaffolded Questions,** TE p. 138 • **Lesson Study Guide,** *Science Study Notebook* p. 66 • **Lesson Quiz,** *Assessment Book* p. 55
	• **Scaffolded Questions,** TE pp. 141, 143 • **Lesson Study Guide,** *Science Study Notebook* p. 67 • **Lesson Quiz,** *Assessment Book* p. 56
marsh	• **Scaffolded Questions,** TE pp. 145, 147 • **Lesson Study Guide,** *Science Study Notebook* p. 68 • **Lesson Quiz,** *Assessment Book* p. 57
	• **Scaffolded Questions,** TE pp. 149, 151 • **Lesson Study Guide,** *Science Study Notebook* p. 69 • **Lesson Quiz,** *Assessment Book* p. 58
Process Skill: Make a Model	• **Explain Your Results,** SE p. 155 • **Activity Recording Sheet,** *Science Study Notebook* pp. 70–71 • **Activity Rubric,** *Science Study Notebook Teacher's Guide* p. T29
	• **Intervention and Reteaching Chart,** TE p. 159 • **Chapter Test,** *Assessment Book* pp. 59–62 • **Success Tracker** www.sfsuccessnet.com
Process Skills: Experiment Hypothesis	• **Tell Your Conclusion,** SE p. 165 • **Activity Recording Sheet,** *Science Study Notebook* pp. 72–73 • **Activity Rubric,** *Science Study Notebook Teacher's Guide* p. T30

DIGITAL CLASSROOM

 Printable Resources
- *Science Study Notebook* pp. 57–73
- *Graphic Organizer 2, TE* pp. EMxxii, EMxxv
- *Intervention Study Guide* pp. 36–47
- *Assessment Book* pp. 51–62
- *Teacher's Activity Guide* pp. 20–22
- LabZone Activities

 AudioText
Unit B, Chapter 5

 eTools
Spreadsheet/Data/Grapher

 Activity Videos
Unit B, Chapter 5

UNIVERSAL ACCESS

English Learners
TE pp. 133, 137, 139, 141, 145, 149

Special Needs
TE pp. 134, 137, 139, 142, 146, 150

Advanced Learners
TE pp. 134, 137, 139, 142, 146, 150

Extra Support
TE pp. 135, 137, 139, 143, 147, 151

CONTENT READERS

 The *Science Content Readers Teacher's Guide* includes California Science Content Standards.

Below-Level   **On-Level**   **Above-Level**

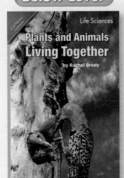  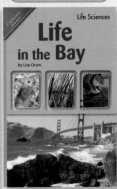

Content Readers deliver the same standards, vocabulary, concepts, and skills as the chapter and can be used for original instruction, reteaching, and enrichment.

Below-Level

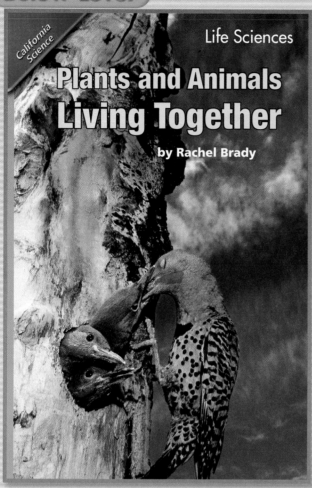

On-Level

Summary

Plants and animals need each other. Plants may need animals to spread seeds. Animals may need plants or other animals for food or shelter. Food chains connect all living things. They start with plants, which make food from sunlight. Some animals eat plants and are, in turn, eaten by larger and larger animals. Each ecosystem has its own food chain. Animals have different teeth depending on what they eat. Carnivores have pointed teeth for tearing meat, while herbivores have flat teeth for chewing and grinding.

Summary

Animals need shelter to keep them safe. Some animals use plants for shelter. Some animals live on other animals. In an environment, a food chain describes how energy is transferred from one organism to another by what the organisms eat. For example, a plant absorbs light from the Sun to make its own food. An aquatic insect eats the plant. Then a squirrel eats the insect. Finally, a bobcat eats the squirrel. You can tell what type of food an animal eats by looking at its teeth. Animals with sharp, pointed teeth eat meat. Animals with flat teeth eat plants.

CONTENT READER DATABASE SUPPORT

www.sfsuccessnet.com

Life Sciences

California Science

Life in the Bay

by Lisa Oram

Use the online database to search for additional content readers by title, content, and target reading skill.

▶ To use the online database, go to **www.sfsuccessnet.com**, and enter your User ID and password from your Teacher Access Pack.

▶ Once logged in, enter the database.

▶ Choose a reading level or a range, or choose other search criteria.

▶ Specify content area, comprehension skill, and/or theme.

▶ Assign text, matching appropriate reading levels for children.

▶ Assign readers to individual children.

▶ Listen to each selection.

▶ Download and print.

▶ Print lesson plans and worksheets for each reader.

Summary

The San Francisco Bay is an estuary. It joins the Sacramento and San Joaquin Rivers to the Pacific Ocean. The water's salinity is influenced by the tides and the weather. Decorator crabs, chinook salmon, and delta smelt live in the bay waters. Many birds, including avocets and the brown pelican, live in the wetlands. Seals and sea lions also live in the bay. Algae, pickleweed, cattails, California poppies, and eel grass are among the plants that live in the bay. People use the bay in many ways. Some human uses harm the bay. The salt marsh harvest mouse is an example of an endangered species. Scientists work to study and protect the bay.

Extended Vocabulary for Above-Level Content Reader

endangered	tides
habitat	wetland

Directed Inquiry

1LS2.c **Life Sciences** Students know animals eat plants or other animals for food and may also use plants or even other animals for shelter and nesting.

1IE4.b **Investigation and Experimentation** Record observations and data with pictures, numbers, or written statements.

Explore ⏱ 10 min
What do animals eat for food?
p. 130

Materials for Small Groups
Matching Cards (Activity Master 2); safety scissors; crayons or markers; glue; construction paper (1 sheet, any color)

Materials listed in *italics* are kit materials.

Alternative Materials
Copier paper can be used instead of construction paper.

Advance Preparation Photocopy the Matching Cards. Use Activity Master 2 from the *Science Study Notebook Teacher's Guide* p. T59.

Tips You may wish to have children color the cards before they cut them out. Have children talk about the matches they made. Encourage them to name each animal and tell what each animal eats. Guide children to infer that some animals eat plants and some animals eat other animals.

What to Expect Children will match the cards to show what different animals eat.

 Activity Video
Unit B, Chapter 5

 Activity Placemat
Mat 10

 Guided Inquiry

1LS2.c **Life Sciences** Students know animals eat plants or other animals for food and may also use plants or even other animals for shelter and nesting.

1IE4.a **Investigation and Experimentation** Draw pictures that portray some features of the thing being described.

1IE4.b **Investigation and Experimentation** Record observations and data with pictures, numbers, or written statements.

Investigate ⏱ 20 min
How can you make a model of a food chain? pp. 154–155

Materials for Small Groups
4 *paper plates; yarn (2 pieces, each about 48 in. long);* crayons or markers; masking tape

Materials listed in *italics* are kit materials.

Alternative Materials
Sheets of white paper may be used in place of paper plates.

Advance Preparation Cut two 4-foot lengths of yarn for each group.

Tips Help children understand that connecting the plates with yarn shows how plants and animals depend on each other through food chains. Discuss with children that the food chain begins with energy from sunlight, which the plants use to make food. Then animals eat food to meet their energy requirements.

What to Expect Children will create food chains showing plants and animals connected in the correct order.

 Activity Video
Unit B, Chapter 5

 Activity Placemat
Mat 11

Lab zone Full Inquiry

1LS2.a **Life Sciences** Students know different plants and animals inhabit different kinds of environments and have external features that help them thrive in different kinds of places.

1IE4.c **Investigation and Experimentation** Record observations on a bar graph.

Experiment ⏱ 20 min

How can color help mice stay hidden from hawks? pp. 164–165

Materials for Small Groups
navy bean seeds ($\frac{1}{2}$ c);
1 Tbsp black-eyed pea bean
seeds; 1 Tbsp black bean seeds;
paper plate; 3 resealable plastic
bags (4 x 6 in.); timer (teacher
use; 1 per class); glue (optional)

Materials listed in *italics* are kit materials.

Advance Preparation For each group, put $\frac{1}{2}$ cup navy bean seeds (white beans) into a resealable plastic bag, 10 black-eyed pea bean seeds (white beans with black spot) into another resealable bag, and 10 black bean seeds into a third resealable bag.

Teaching Tips The teacher should say "Go" and "Stop" so that the hawk knows when to pick up the mice. Each hawk gets 15 seconds to pick up the mice using only one hand. Each time there is a new hawk, be sure that there are 10 black beans and 10 white beans with spots on the plate. Children may glue the beans onto their graph.

What to Expect Children will find it harder to see the white beans with black spots.

 Activity Video
Unit B, Chapter 5

 Activity Placemat
Mat 12

Additional Activity Resources

The following resources are available for activities found in the Student Edition.

 Printable Resources

▸ *Science Study Notebook*
  • Activity Recording Sheets
    Recording sheets provide structure to help children record data from each activity.
  • Activity Rubrics
    Teachers can monitor children's progress using the Activity Rubric in the *Science Study Notebook Teacher's Guide.*
▸ *Teacher's Activity Guide* For detailed information about Inquiry Activities, access the *Teacher's Activity Guide* at **www.sfsuccessnet.com**.

 Activity Videos
Prepare for and rehearse each activity before class by watching a video of the activity.

> *"As students progress through the three stages of inquiry, support from the teacher diminishes and student ownership increases."*
>
> —Dr. Karen Ostlund, UTeach, College of Natural Sciences, The University of Texas at Austin

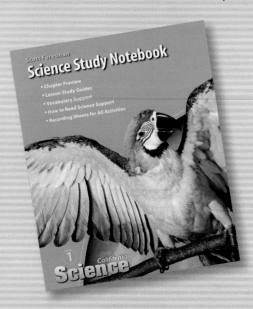

▶ **Chapter Study Guide**
Children preview and organize the key concepts in the chapter.

▶ **Chapter Vocabulary Cards** Children cut out cards to use with suggested strategies in the Teacher's Edition.

▶ **Chapter Vocabulary Preview** Children are introduced to science words.

▶ **How to Read Science** Children record answers for the Student Edition page.

▶ **Lesson Study Guides** Children practice note-taking as they learn key concepts while reading.

▶ **Inquiry Activities** *Science Study Notebook Teacher's Guide* provides an Activity Rubric to evaluate children's progress.

▶ **Printable Resources** All pages of the *Science Study Notebook* are available to purchasers of Scott Foresman California Science ©2008 at **www.sfsuccessnet.com**.

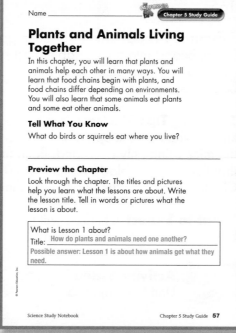

CHAPTER 5 STUDY GUIDE
Science Study Notebook, p. 57

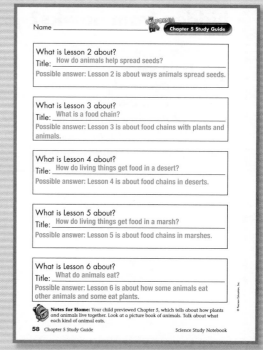

CHAPTER 5 STUDY GUIDE
Science Study Notebook, p. 58

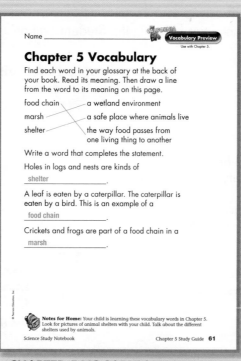

CHAPTER 5 VOCABULARY PREVIEW
Science Study Notebook, p. 61

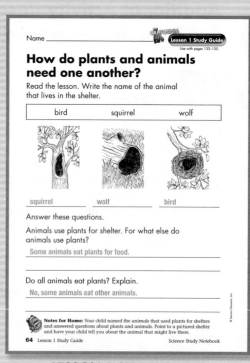

LESSON 1 STUDY GUIDE
Science Study Notebook, p. 64

> *"The Science Study Notebook serves as the important link between science and literacy when used in the classroom as a knowledge-transforming form of writing."*
>
> —Michael Klentschy, Superintendent of El Centro Elementary School District, El Centro, California

---

Name _____

Lesson 2 Study Guide
Use with pages 136–137.

How do animals spread seeds?

Read the lesson. For each set, put the sentences in the order they happen. Number them 1, 2, 3.

2	With the seed on its fur, the bear moves around.
3	The seed falls off the bear.
1	A seed sticks to a bear's fur.

3	A tree might grow from the buried acorn.
1	A squirrel picks up an acorn.
2	The squirrel buries the acorn.

Notes for Home: Your child showed the sequence of animals spreading seeds. Use a self-stick note to demonstrate how seeds can spread. Attach a note to your clothing. Remove the note in another room. Talk with your child about how seeds spread.

Science Study Notebook   Lesson 2 Study Guide **65**

LESSON 2 STUDY GUIDE
Science Study Notebook, p. 65

Name _____

Lesson 3 Study Guide
Use with pages 138–139.

What is a food chain?

Read the lesson. Put the sentences where they fit in the food chain.

A caterpillar eats the leaves of the plant.
A bird eats the caterpillar.
A plant uses sunlight to make food.

A plant uses sunlight to make food.

↓

A caterpillar eats the leaves of the plant.

↓

A bird eats the caterpillar.

Notes for Home: Your child identified a food chain. Encourage your child to tell you about the food chain. Then talk about other food chains.

66   Lesson 3 Study Guide   Science Study Notebook

LESSON 3 STUDY GUIDE
Science Study Notebook, p. 66

Name _____

Lesson 4 Study Guide
Use with pages 140–143.

How do living things get food in a desert?

Read the lesson. Use the words in the box to complete the sentences.

coyote	environment	food chain
insects	lizard	roadrunner	sunlight

1. A desert is an __environment__ .
2. Desert plants use __sunlight__ to make food.
3. Some __insects__ eat the plants as food.
4. A __lizard__ eats the insects as food.
5. A __roadrunner__ eats the lizard as food.
6. A __coyote__ eats the roadrunner as food.
7. The plants and animals are part of a desert __food chain__ .

Notes for Home: Your child completed sentences about a desert food chain. Help your child sequence the events in the food chain.

Science Study Notebook   Lesson 4 Study Guide **67**

LESSON 4 STUDY GUIDE
Science Study Notebook, p. 67

Name _____

Lesson 5 Study Guide
Use with pages 144–147.

How do living things get food in a marsh?

Read the lesson. Answer the question.

What is a marsh?
__a wetland environment__

Put the plants and animals where they belong in the food chain.

cricket   frog   grass   hawk   snake

grass

↓

cricket

↓

frog

↓

snake

↓

hawk

Notes for Home: Your child identified a food chain in a marsh. Write the names of the animals and plant on cards. Mix the cards and ask your child to arrange them to show the food chain.

68   Lesson 5 Study Guide   Science Study Notebook

LESSON 5 STUDY GUIDE
Science Study Notebook, p. 68

Name _____

Lesson 6 Study Guide
Use with pages 148–151.

What do animals eat?

Read the lesson. Circle the term that makes the sentence true. Write the term on the line.

1. Some animals that eat plants have __flat__ teeth?
   (flat)   sharp, pointed

2. Some animals that eat other animals have __sharp, pointed__ teeth?
   flat   (sharp, pointed)

Write the name of the animal where it belongs in the chart.

Tigers have sharp, pointed teeth.
Sheep have flat teeth.
Lions have sharp, pointed teeth.
Deer have flat teeth.
Cows have flat teeth.
Wolves have sharp, pointed teeth.

Animals that eat plants	Animals that eat other animals
sheep	tigers
deer	lions
cows	wolves

Notes for Home: Your child identified animals as plant eaters or meat eaters. Name an animal in the chart and have your child tell you what it eats.

Science Study Notebook   Lesson 6 Study Guide **69**

LESSON 6 STUDY GUIDE
Science Study Notebook, p. 69

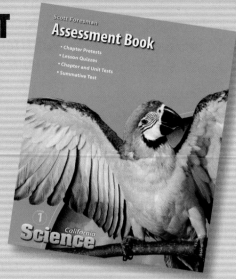

Scott Foresman
Assessment Book
- Chapter Pretests
- Lesson Quizzes
- Chapter and Unit Tests
- Summative Test

California
Science

DIGITAL **Printable Resources** All pages of the *Assessment Book* are available to purchasers of Scott Foresman California Science ©2008 at www.sfsuccessnet.com.

Name _____

CALIFORNIA
Chapter 5 Pretest

Read each question and choose the best answer. Then fill in the circle next to the correct answer.

1 What do plants need to grow?
- Ⓐ light
- Ⓑ meat
- Ⓒ fruit
- Ⓓ flowers

2 Look at the picture.

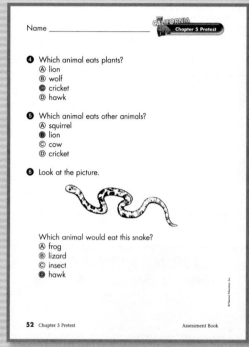

Which animal lives here?
- Ⓐ a wolf
- Ⓑ a bear
- Ⓒ a lizard
- Ⓓ a bird

3 What do animals eat with?
- Ⓐ legs
- Ⓑ teeth
- Ⓒ eyes
- Ⓓ ears

Assessment Book Chapter 5 Pretest **51**

CHAPTER 5 PRETEST
Assessment Book, p. 51

Name _____

CALIFORNIA
Chapter 5 Pretest

4 Which animal eats plants?
- Ⓐ lion
- Ⓑ wolf
- Ⓒ cricket
- Ⓓ hawk

5 Which animal eats other animals?
- Ⓐ squirrel
- Ⓑ lion
- Ⓒ cow
- Ⓓ cricket

6 Look at the picture.

Which animal would eat this snake?
- Ⓐ frog
- Ⓑ lizard
- Ⓒ insect
- Ⓓ hawk

52 Chapter 5 Pretest Assessment Book

CHAPTER 5 PRETEST
Assessment Book, p. 52

Name _____

CALIFORNIA
Lesson 1 Quiz
Use with pages 133–135.

Complete the Sentence
Write the word that completes each sentence.

animals	food	nests	shelter

1. A place where an animal lives is a ___shelter___.

2. Some animals eat plants for ___food___.

3. Some animals eat other ___animals___.

4. Some animals make ___nests___ in plants.

Apply What You Learned
5. Color the animals that use plants for shelter.

Bird	**Flea**	**Squirrel**

bird and squirrel

Assessment Book Lesson 1 Quiz **53**

LESSON 1 QUIZ
Assessment Book, p. 53

Name _____

CALIFORNIA
Lesson 2 Quiz
Use with pages 136–137.

Complete the Sentence
Write the word that completes each sentence.

fur	grow	plant	seeds

1. Some animals spread ___plant___ seeds.

2. Seeds can stick to the ___fur___ on a bear.

3. Birds drop and spread ___seeds___.

4. New plants may ___grow___ from these seeds.

Apply What You Learned
5. How do squirrels help new oak trees grow?

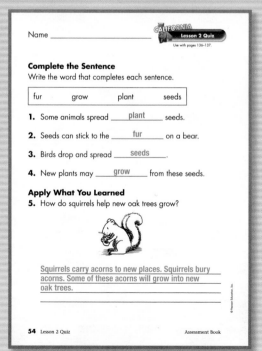

Squirrels carry acorns to new places. Squirrels bury acorns. Some of these acorns will grow into new oak trees.

54 Lesson 2 Quiz Assessment Book

LESSON 2 QUIZ
Assessment Book, p. 54

Name _____

CALIFORNIA
Lesson 3 Quiz
Use with pages 138–129.

Complete the Sentence
Write the word that completes each sentence.

animals	food chains	plants	Sun

1. Plants take in light from the ___Sun___ to make food.

2. Some ___animals___ eat plants for food.

3. Some animals eat other animals that eat ___plants___.

4. All living things are connected through ___food chains___.

Apply What You Learned
5. Draw arrows to show how food moves in the food chain. Then write to tell what happens.

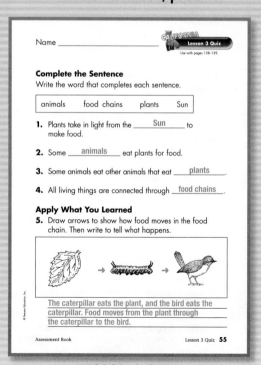

The caterpillar eats the plant, and the bird eats the caterpillar. Food moves from the plant through the caterpillar to the bird.

Assessment Book Lesson 3 Quiz **55**

LESSON 3 QUIZ
Assessment Book, p. 55

Name _____

CALIFORNIA
Lesson 4 Quiz
Use with pages 140–143.

Complete the Sentence
Write the word that completes each sentence.

animals	food	insects	sunlight

1. Plants need ___sunlight___ to grow.

2. Plants use sunlight to make ___food___.

3. Some ___insects___ eat plants for food.

4. A coyote eats other ___animals___ for food.

Apply What You Learned
5. Tell why a desert coyote could not live if there were no plants.

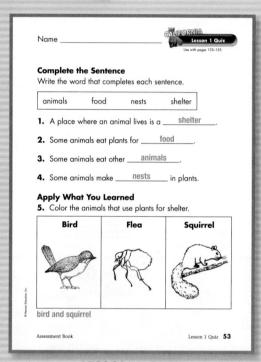

Plants use sunlight to make food. Coyotes could not live without plants because plants start the food chain.

56 Lesson 4 Quiz Assessment Book

LESSON 4 QUIZ
Assessment Book, p. 56

Entry-Level Assessment

▶ **Assessment Book:**
Chapter 5 Pretest

Progress-Monitoring Assessment

Ongoing Assessment
▶ **Student Edition:**
Checkpoint and Lesson Review questions
▶ **Teacher's Edition:**
Diagnostic Check and Scaffolded Questions
▶ **Assessment Book:**
Lesson Quizzes

▶ **DIGITAL Success Tracker** Chapter 5 online assessment and reteaching

Formal Assessment
▶ **Student Edition:**
Chapter 5 Review/Test
▶ **DIGITAL ExamView** Customizable Chapter 5 Test

Summative Assessment

▶ **Student Edition:**
Unit B California Standards Practice
▶ **Assessment Book:**
Chapter 5 Test
Unit B Test
Summative Test

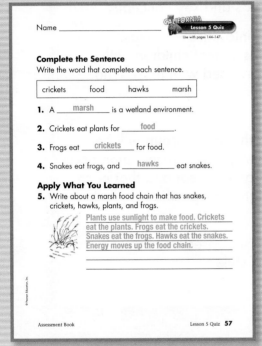

LESSON 5 QUIZ
Assessment Book, p. 57

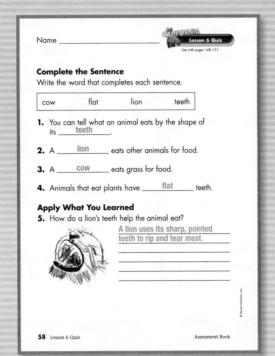

LESSON 6 QUIZ
Assessment Book, p. 58

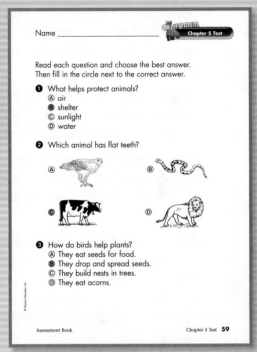

CHAPTER 5 TEST
Assessment Book, p. 59

CHAPTER 5 TEST
Assessment Book, p. 60

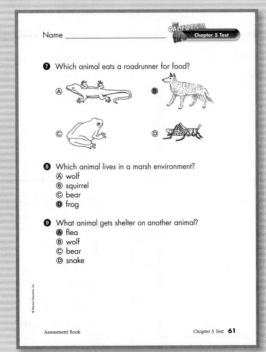

CHAPTER 5 TEST
Assessment Book, p. 61

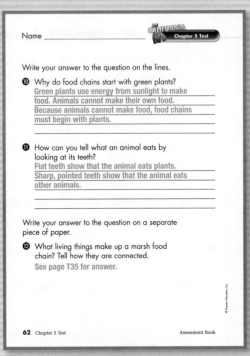

CHAPTER 5 TEST
Assessment Book, p. 62

Strategies

Use these suggested strategies to help you customize instruction for children with individual needs.

Strategies for
English Learners

Grammar in Action

▶ Show children objects, or demonstrate actions or ideas. Name and use them in sentences. Demonstrate the meaning of other words, including high frequency words such as *a/the* and *and/but*. Model verb tense changes or other points of grammar.

▶ **Beginning** Model a basic English sentence pattern, such as *This is a _____*. Have children repeat and form similar sentences.

▶ **Intermediate** Model a sentence pattern frequently found in science, such as *If _____, then _____*. Have children use the pattern to make new sentences.

▶ **Advanced** Ask groups of children to discuss and write a paragraph about an important lesson concept. Review the writings, and suggest ways to enhance grammar usage.

Strategies for
Special Needs

Jigsaw Groups

▶ Review the chapter essential question with children. Help children to identify and define the vocabulary words and key concepts.

▶ Organize the class into jigsaw groups. Construct the groups so that children with special needs are grouped with those who have a variety of learning styles and skill levels.

▶ Explain to children that each group will be responsible for developing a presentation on what two different animals eat and that each person will be assigned a specific task within the group.

▶ Assign individual tasks based on a child's ability and learning style.

Strategies for
Advanced Learners

Technology Apprentice

▶ Review the big idea of the chapter with children. Have children identify the key concepts in the chapter.

▶ Invite children to prepare a multimedia presentation on one of the topics in the chapter, such as how plants and animals need one another, what a food chain is, or what animals eat. If necessary, pair or group children on a particular topic.

▶ Guide children as they research their topics. Have them work with the media specialist to plan and produce their multimedia presentations.

▶ Encourage children to share their presentations with the class.

Strategies for
Extra Support

Compare and Contrast

▶ Examine the chapter's illustrations, captions, lesson focus questions, headings, and boldface vocabulary terms with children.

▶ While reading the chapter, have children use a Venn diagram to list the similarities and differences between how plants and animals get food in a marsh environment. Before children begin reading, model the assignment using a Venn diagram.

▶ Encourage volunteers to share their Venn diagrams with the class. Discuss the similarities and differences between how plants and animals get food in a marsh environment.

Integrated Universal Access

	English Learners	Special Needs	Advanced Learners	Extra Support
1LS2.c Students know animals eat plants or other animals for food and may also use plants or even other animals for shelter and nesting.	**Describe Shelters** TE p. 133	**Make a Nest** TE p. 134	**Learn More About Animal Shelters** TE p. 134	**Solve Puzzles** TE p. 135
	Describe How Seeds Are Moved TE p. 137	**Hoop and Loop Fastener Model** TE p. 137	**Identify Animals That Spread Seeds** TE p. 137	**Dramatize the Movement of Seeds** TE p. 137
	Explain a Food Chain TE p. 139	**Pictures of Animals Eating** TE p. 139	**Identify a Food Chain** TE p. 139	**Make a Food "Chain"** TE p. 139
	Put a Food Chain in Order TE p. 141	**Draw an Animal and Its Food** TE p. 142	**Sing a Food Chain Song** TE p. 142	**Make a Desert Mural** TE p. 143
	Marsh Food Chains TE p. 145	**Sequencing a Food Chain** TE p. 146	**Marsh Research Project** TE p. 146	**Make a Book** TE p. 147
1LS2.d Students know how to infer what animals eat from the shape of their teeth (e.g., sharp teeth: eats meat; flat teeth: eats plants).	**Animals' Teeth and What They Eat** TE p. 149	**Make a Model of Teeth** TE p. 150	**Which Teeth Are Used for What** TE p. 150	**Observe Teeth** TE p. 151

California English-Language Arts
CONTENT STANDARDS FOCUS

1RW1.0 **Word Analysis, Fluency, and Systematic Vocabulary Development** Students understand the basic features of reading. They select patterns and know how to translate them into spoken language by using phonics, syllabication, and word parts. They apply this knowledge to achieve fluent oral and silent reading.

Objective Students determine meaning and increase vocabulary as they read science.

Focus on the Big Idea 🕐 20 min

Chapter 5 Vocabulary Terms
shelter, p. 134
food chain, p. 138
marsh, p. 144

Printable Pretest Assess children's background knowledge with Chapter 5 Pretest on *Assessment Book* pp. 51–52.

1. Build Background

Warm Up
Activate Prior Knowledge

▶ Ask children the essential question, *How do plants and animals live together?* Save responses for later in the chapter.

▶ Ask children to tell what they know about how plants and animals live together. List their responses on the board.

2. Introduce Vocabulary

Preview Terms
Printable Graphic Organizer Use *Graphic Organizer 7* (TE p. EMxxv) to focus children's attention on science vocabulary as they read Chapter 5.

▶ Many science vocabulary words are abstract. Use the pictures and labels on these pages to help you open a discussion about science concepts and build academic language.

▶ List the vocabulary terms on the board. Have children pronounce each word as you write it.

▶ Discuss the meaning of each word and how it relates to how plants and animals live together.

Focus on the BIG Idea

How do plants and animals live together?

shelter

marsh

food chain

128

Big Idea
All living organisms in an environment are interdependent.

Teacher Background

▶ Food chains are one way plants and animals are linked. Many animals eat a variety of plants and animals. Therefore, simple food chains often are linked to other food chains. This forms large, complex food webs. Regardless of the size of a food chain or the complexity of a food web, plants are the primary food source.

▶ Animals also use plants or even other animals for shelter or nesting.

▶ Some animals assist plant reproduction by spreading seeds or pollinating flowers.

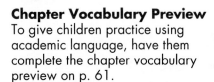

Chapter 5 Vocabulary

shelter page 134

food chain page 138

marsh page 144

129

Share and Talk

Use questions such as the following to help children clarify their understanding of vocabulary terms.

▶ What might happen if the wolf pup did not have a shelter? Possible answer: It might not stay safe.

▶ Marshes have water. What kinds of animals probably live in marshes? Possible answer: Animals that are suited to living in and around water, such as frogs, turtles, and some insects.

Science Study Notebook
Printable Resources

Chapter Vocabulary Preview
To give children practice using academic language, have them complete the chapter vocabulary preview on p. 61.

Vocabulary Cards Have children use the vocabulary cards on pp. 59–60 to play a sentence game. Children should take turns choosing vocabulary cards and using the vocabulary terms in a sentence.

3. Practice

Active Glossary Reinforce science vocabulary and concepts with Active Glossary animations.

Vocabulary Strategy

Unfamiliar Words Tell children that they can often understand an unfamiliar word by reading the words in the sentence near the unfamiliar word. Other words in the sentence can give clues about the word's meaning. Write this sentence on the board: *The marsh is very wet.*

Ask: What do you think a marsh is? Possible answer: A marsh is a kind of environment that has water. Help children to understand how the word *wet* can explain what a marsh is.

1LS2.c Life Sciences Students know animals eat plants or other animals for food and may also use plants or even other animals for shelter and nesting.

1IE4.b Investigation and Experimentation Record observations and data with pictures, numbers, or written statements.

Objective Students infer that animals eat plants or other animals.

Directed Inquiry   🕙 10 min

1. Get Ready

Materials for Small Groups

Matching Cards   crayons or markers
(Activity Master 2)
                                  glue
safety scissors   construction paper

Materials listed in *italics* are kit materials.

Alternative Materials Copier paper can be used instead of construction paper.

2. What to Do

Preview

▶ Conduct an inventory of materials with children. For English Learners, solicit alternative names for items in their home language. Post names of materials and other academic language, such as *infer*, on a word wall.

▶ You may wish to preview science content in Lesson 3.

Advance Preparation Photocopy the Matching Cards. Use Activity Master 2 from *Science Study Notebook Teacher's Guide* p. T59.

Tips Have children talk about the matches they made. Guide children to infer that some animals eat plants, and some animals eat other animals.

Safety Remind children to use scissors carefully.

3. Explain Your Results

Science Study Notebook
 **Printable Resources
Activity Recording Sheet**
Discuss the results of the activity by reviewing completed p. 62. Ask volunteers to describe the matches they made. What kinds of things do animals eat?

Activity Rubric Use *Science Study Notebook Teacher's Guide* p. T28 to evaluate children's work.

Lab zone Directed Inquiry

Explore What do animals eat for food?

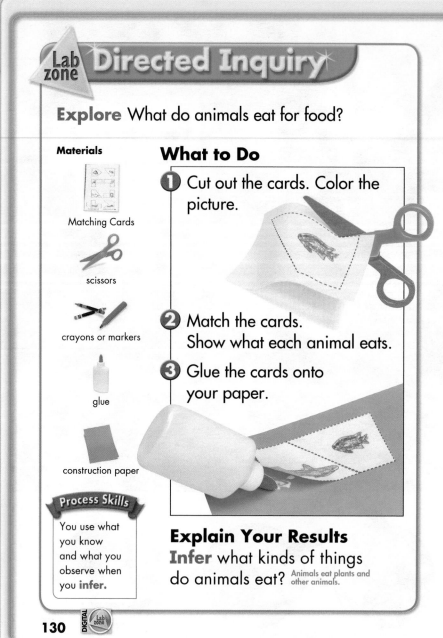

Materials

Matching Cards

scissors

crayons or markers

glue

construction paper

Process Skills

You use what you know and what you observe when you **infer**.

What to Do

❶ Cut out the cards. Color the picture.

❷ Match the cards. Show what each animal eats.

❸ Glue the cards onto your paper.

Explain Your Results
Infer what kinds of things do animals eat? Animals eat plants and other animals.

130

Digital Classroom

Activity Video Prepare for and rehearse the activity before class.

Printable Activity Rubric Monitor children's progress using the Activity Rubric located at **www.sfsuccessnet.com**.

Printable LabZone Activity Provide children with additional activities located at **www.sfsuccessnet.com**.

Call **1-888-537-4908** with activity questions.

Big Idea	Teacher Background
Animals eat plants and other animals as food.	▶ Some animals eat only meat (carnivores), some eat only plants (herbivores), and some, like human beings, eat both plants and meat (omnivores). All animals must eat food to meet their energy requirements and to obtain the nutrients that they need to grow and stay healthy.

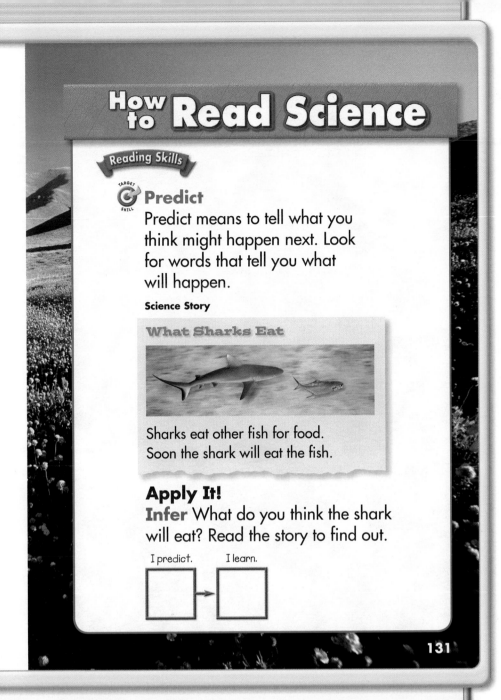

How to Read Science

Reading Skills

Predict

Predict means to tell what you think might happen next. Look for words that tell you what will happen.

Science Story

What Sharks Eat

Sharks eat other fish for food. Soon the shark will eat the fish.

Apply It!

Infer What do you think the shark will eat? Read the story to find out.

I predict.   I learn.

131

English-Language Arts Support

1RC2.5 Reading Comprehension

▶ **Printable Graphic Organizer** Use *Graphic Organizer 4* (TE p. EMxxii) with children to help them understand how to predict what will happen next and then to find words that can confirm their predictions.

▶ To help meet the needs of children whose reading skills are below grade level, provide extra practice making predictions. Describe several situations and have children predict what will happen next. For example: A dog sees a cat (prediction: the dog will chase it).

California English-Language Arts
CONTENT STANDARDS FOCUS

1RC2.5 Reading Comprehension Confirm predictions about what will happen next in a text by identifying key words (i.e., signpost words).

Objective Students make and confirm predictions while reading a science story.

How to Read Science 25 min

1. Build Background

Comprehension Skill: Predict

Tell children that predicting means to tell what they think will happen next. Before reading, have children look at the picture on p. 131.

Ask: What is happening in the picture? What do you think might happen next? The shark is chasing another fish. The shark will catch the fish.

2. Teach

What Sharks Eat

Read the title of the story aloud with the children. Then ask them to predict what they think will happen next. Read aloud the story. Remind them to listen carefully for details during reading that may change or confirm predictions. Discuss their original predictions and compare them with the content of the story. Tell children that sharks eat marine mammals in addition to fish.

Science Study Notebook

Printable Recording Sheet To help children understand how to make and confirm predictions, have them complete the How to Read Science recording sheet on p. 63.

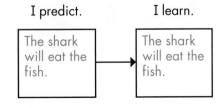

3. Summarize and Assess

Apply It!

Predict involves stating what children think will happen next. Work with children to make and confirm predictions about the science story, "What Sharks Eat."

I predict.   I learn.

| The shark will eat the fish. | → | The shark will eat the fish. |

Life Sciences Students know animals eat plants or other animals for food and may also use plants or even other animals for shelter and nesting.

Objective Students tell what a shelter is and explain how animals are dependent upon plants and other animals.

Chapter 5   Lesson 1   30 min

How do plants and animals need one another?

1. Build Background

Printable Pretest Assess children's background knowledge with Chapter 5 Pretest on *Assessment Book* pp. 51–52.

Science Song Listen to the song "Good Partners." Discuss what it means if two people or things are good partners. (They work well together; they share.) Ask children to think of some examples of people, animals, or things that are good partners.

Standards Warm Up

Activate Prior Knowledge Ask children to think about where they live. Write a list on the board of the different types of homes in which they live (e.g., houses, apartments, mobile homes). Discuss with children why they need a place to live.

2. Teach

⮞ QUICK Plan

▶ As a class, take a picture walk through the lesson to discuss visuals and captions.

▶ **AudioText** Use the audio version of the Student Edition at a technology center.

▶ Encourage children to work in teams to answer lesson questions.

Science Study Notebook

Printable Chapter Study Guide Have children check their understanding of Chapter 5 by completing pp. 57–58 as they read.

You Are There

Good Partners

Sung to the tune of "Frère Jacques"
Lyrics by Gerri Brioso & Richard Freitas/The Dovetail Group, Inc.

Plants and animals,
Are good partners.
Yes, they are.
Yes, they are.
Plants can be a shelter,
For animals to live in.
That's a fact.
That's a fact.

132

Big Idea	Teacher Background
Animals use plants for many purposes.	▶ Many birds use plants for food and as places to seek refuge from inclement weather and predators. Birds build their nests using materials and plants from their environments. **Common Misconception** Children might think that only birds build nests. However, other animals make nests too. For example, squirrels and rabbits make nests. Help children to understand that nests can be made of other natural materials besides plants, such as sand, mud, feathers, or even spiderwebs.

Lesson 1

How do plants and animals need one another?

Did you know that plants and animals need each other to live? Plants grow almost everywhere in the world.

Some animals eat plants for food. Some animals eat other animals. Some animals make nests in plants. Some animals even make nests on other animals.

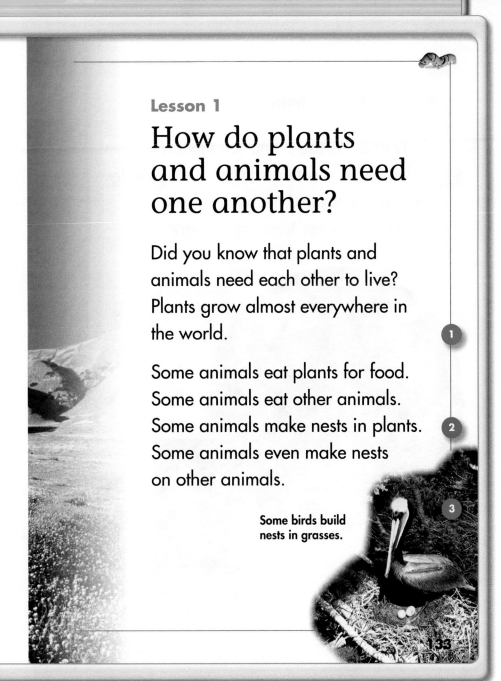

Some birds build nests in grasses.

Universal Access

English Learners
Describe Shelters Have children identify animals and their shelters as you read a book such as *Castles, Caves, and Honeycombs* by Linda Ashman (ISBN: 0-15-202211-2).

LSB1 ELD Listening and Speaking
Beginning Read through the book again with children and identify the names of the animals and their shelters that appear on each page. Review with children until they can name the animals independently.

REI8 ELD Reading
Intermediate Ask children to draw one animal they are familiar with in its shelter. Review some of the animals and shelters shown in the book. Have children discuss their pictures in pairs.

LSA1 ELD Listening and Speaking
Advanced Have children use stick-on notes to cover the text in the book. Model how to write text for the first page. Have children write new text for various pages. Ask volunteers to read what they wrote.

English-Language Arts Support
1RW1.17 Word Analysis, Fluency, and Systematic Vocabulary Development

▶ After reading the lesson, ask children to classify animals into two groups: animals that eat plants, and animals that eat other animals. Encourage children to think of animals and help them classify the animals by what they eat.

▶ Use a T-chart to help children classify the animals. Children who need extra support may use the completed T-chart as a study aid as they complete the chapter.

Scaffolded Questions

Use the following guiding questions to monitor children's comprehension.

1 **Recall** Where do plants grow? Plants grow almost everywhere in the world.

2 **Apply** What are two ways animals use plants? Animals use plants for food and for places to make nests.

3 **Propose** What does the bird eat if it doesn't eat plants? The bird eats other animals such as insects or fish.

Extend Science Vocabulary

▶ Have children locate the word *nests* on p. 133. Tell children that some animals build nests for shelter.

▶ Explain that *nest* can be used to describe both the shelter that an animal builds and the act of building or living in the shelter.

▶ Ask the children to complete the sentences:
The bird built a _____.
The squirrels _____ in the tree.

▶ Discuss how the word *nest* is used in each sentence.

Diagnostic Check

If . . . children have difficulty understanding how plants and animals need each other to live,

then . . . discuss animals they are familiar with and invite children to talk about what these animals eat and where they live.

Science Study Notebook

Printable Lesson Study Guide
Have children check their understanding of Lesson 1 by completing p. 64 as they read.

Share and Talk

Review what animals need to live (food, water, and air). Read pp. 134–135 with children. Discuss what shelters provide for animals. (Shelters give animals a place for babies to grow, protection from the weather, and a safe hiding place from other animals.) Encourage children to identify where different animals build nests and find shelter.

Ask: What are some nests made of? Possible answers: Plants, twigs, sticks, leaves, grass, soil

Write About Science

1WA2.2 **Writing Applications** Have children choose one of the animals on pp. 134–135 and describe its shelter in two or three sentences, using descriptive details.

Writing Rubric

4	The child's sentences focus on one animal and its shelter. The shelter is described accurately and the writer includes many descriptive details. There are very few errors.
3	The child's sentences focus on one animal and its shelter. The writer includes some descriptive details. There are some errors.
2	The child's sentences lack focus and may be incomplete. The writer includes few details describing a shelter. There are many errors.
1	The child's sentences are incomplete and do not focus on a shelter. The writer includes no details that describe a shelter.

Tip

Before children begin writing, make a list of the animals and their shelters on the board. Then choose an animal from the list and model how to write sentences describing the animal's shelter.

Animals Need Shelter

Many animals use plants for shelter.
1 A **shelter** is a safe place for animals to live.
Some animals build nests for shelter.
Some animals use trees for shelter.

Some birds build nests in shrubs.

Some birds build nests in trees.

Some squirrels use trees as shelter.

134

Universal Access

Special Needs

Make a Nest Give children disposable bowls and art supplies such as pieces of yarn, craft sticks, glue, and whole, torn, and shredded paper in different weights and textures. Ask children to make models of nests. Encourage children also to make or draw birds or other animals for their nests. Allow children to describe their models.

Advanced Learners

Learn More About Animal Shelters Show children pictures of different animal shelters. Have them try to identify the animal that lives in each shelter by using clues in the pictures. Encourage children to use the library media center to find more information about animal shelters. Let volunteers share their information with the class.

Some animals use other animals
for shelter.
Fleas use other animals for shelter.

 **Lesson Review**

1. What is a shelter?
   1. A shelter is a safe place
   for animals to live.

2.  **Writing in Science** Write a
   sentence. Tell where animals might
   nest or find shelter.
   2. Answers will vary. Possible
   answer: Animals might nest
   or find shelter in shrubs, in
   trees, and on other animals.

**Fleas nest
and live
on other
animals.**

**What does
the wolf
cub use for
shelter?**

135

Universal Access

Extra Support
Solve Puzzles Have children fold a piece of paper in half. On
one side, have them draw an animal shown in the lesson. On the
other side, have them draw the animal's shelter. Have them cut the
paper on the fold. Then, mix up the children's pictures. Have children
work together to match the animals to their shelters. Discuss with
children which animals use plants for shelter.

Use the following guiding questions to monitor children's
comprehension.

1. **Define** What is a shelter? A shelter is a safe place
   for animals to live.

2. **Classify** Which animals on pp. 134–135 use plants
   for shelter or nests? The birds, squirrel, and wolf cub
   use plants for shelter or nests.

3. **Compare** How is the shelter of the wolf pup
   different from the shelter of the flea? Possible answer:
   The wolf pup uses a log or plant as shelter, and the
   flea uses the wolf pup or another animal as shelter.

Extend Science Vocabulary

▶ Review the meaning of the vocabulary word **shelter**
   with children.

▶ Have children name and draw pictures of different
   animals' shelters. Ask children to explain how the
   shelters are similar to their own homes, as shelters.

▶ Lead children in a discussion of how animals' shelters
   keep them safe. (Possible answers: By protecting
   animals from rain, cold, other animals, heat in a hot
   climate, snow in a cold climate, and so on)

▶ **Active Glossary** Children who need more
   practice with vocabulary terms may review
   vocabulary online or use vocabulary cards (*Science
   Study Notebook*, pp. 59–60).

3. Summarize and Assess

QUICK Summary

▶ Plants and animals need each other to live.

▶ A shelter is a safe place where an animal lives.

▶ Animals use plants and other animals for shelter and
   nests.

Assess
Printable Resources

Lesson Quiz Check for understanding
by reviewing children's responses
to *Assessment Book* p. 53 or to the
Lesson Review in the Student Edition.

Intervention Study Guide Use pp. 36–37 to
review and reinforce lesson concepts as needed.

California Science
CONTENT STANDARDS FOCUS

1LS2.c **Life Sciences** Students know animals eat plants or other animals for food and may also use plants or even other animals for shelter and nesting.

Objective Students describe another way plants and animals are interdependent.

Chapter 5   Lesson 2  20 min

How do animals help spread seeds?

1. Build Background

Standards Warm Up

Activate Prior Knowledge Bring in different types of seeds, such as bean seeds, pumpkin seeds, and apple seeds, to show children. Ask them to describe what they would need to do with the seeds to make them grow (plant and water them).

2. Teach

Science Study Notebook

 **Printable Lesson Study Guide**
Have children check their understanding of Lesson 2 by completing p. 65 as they read.

Share and Talk

Review with children how plants grow from seeds. Have children point to the different seeds on pp. 136–137. Talk about how some animals carry the seeds from one place to another. Have children discuss where they have seen seeds (in an apple, in a pumpkin, on the ground, in a tree).

Scaffolded Questions

Use the following guiding questions to monitor children's comprehension.

1 **Recall** What animals might spread seeds? Possible answers: Bears, squirrels, and birds might spread seeds.

2 **Explain** Tell how seeds might be spread by a bear. A bear rubs against a plant with seeds, and the seeds stick to its fur. The bear carries the seeds and they fall to the ground in a new place.

3 **Analyze** What would happen if animals did not help spread seeds? Possible answer: Not as many seeds would grow in new places.

Lesson 2

How do animals help spread seeds?

Plants and animals need each other.
Some animals spread plant seeds.
Some animals carry seeds to new places.
New plants may grow from these seeds.

Seeds might stick to the fur on the bear. The bear moves the **2** seeds to new places.

136

Big Idea	Teacher Background
Animals disperse seeds from the fruits of plants they eat.	▸ Some plants depend on animals to eat their fruits and spread their seeds. Many plants produce fruits that attract animals. When animals eat these fruits they often ingest the seeds. The seeds travel through the animals' digestive systems and are deposited in new locations when the animals produce waste. These seeds may grow into new plants if the conditions are appropriate.

The squirrel carries an acorn to a new place.

The acorn might grow into a new oak tree.

Squirrels bury some acorns in the ground. Oak trees may grow from these acorns.

Birds drop and spread seeds too.

✓ **Lesson Review**

1. How do some animals help plants?

   1. Possible answer: Animals help plants spread seeds.

2. 🖉 **Writing in Science** Write two sentences to tell how animals might spread seeds.

   2. Answers will vary. Possible answer: The seeds stick to the fur of the animal. The animal carries the seeds to new places.

137

▶ Write the word *spread* on the board. Explain that *spread* means "to stretch out or scatter something over a larger area."

▶ Ask children to share a time when they have spread something (fruit preserves on bread, paint on paper, spilled beads on the floor).

▶ Explain to children that animals help plants by spreading their seeds to new places. Ask children if they can think of other ways seeds are spread to new places. (The wind can blow seeds, or people can carry seeds to new places.)

3. Summarize and Assess

QUICK Summary

▶ Plants and animals need one another.

▶ Animals carry seeds from place to place.

Assess

Printable Resources

Lesson Quiz Check for understanding by reviewing children's responses to *Assessment Book* p. 54 or to the Lesson Review in the Student Edition.

Intervention Study Guide Use pp. 38–39 to review and reinforce lesson concepts as needed.

Universal Access

English Learners
Describe How Seeds Are Moved Review the names of the animals on pp. 136–137. Identify parts of the animals (such as fur, feet, mouth, or beak) that help carry the seeds to new places.

LSB1 ELD Listening and Speaking
Beginning Point to the bear and say, "The bear carries seeds." Have children repeat the sentence. Repeat this exercise by pointing to the other animals and telling how they spread seeds.

LS11 ELD Listening and Speaking
Intermediate Describe how a bear spreads seeds using sentences such as "Seeds stick to the bear's fur. Then the seeds fall off." Have children repeat the sentences and tell how other animals spread seeds.

REA10 ELD Reading
Advanced Reread pp. 136–137 with children. Have children use this cloze sentence to tell how the animals spread seeds: *The _____ spreads seeds using its _____.*

Advanced Learners
Identify Animals That Spread Seeds Allow small groups of children to look through books about animals to find other animals that might spread seeds. For example, children might notice that dogs have fur, and from that children could infer that dogs can move seeds. Ask each child to draw a picture and write a caption about how one of the identified animals spreads seeds. Invite children to share their work.

Extra Support
Dramatize the Movement of Seeds Allow each child to pretend that he or she is one of the animals on pp. 136–137. Have children act out how the animals move seeds. Have children make props for their dramatization.

Special Needs
Hook and Loop Fastener Model To help children understand how seeds attach to fur, cut pieces of fastener. Have children feel the rough side of the fastener. Tell children that some seeds are similar to this fastener, and explain that just as it can stick to things, some seeds can stick. Have children try to stick the fastener on their clothing. As they remove the fastener, explain to children that seeds eventually drop or rub off animals' fur.

1LS2.c **Life Sciences** Students know animals eat plants or other animals for food and may also use plants or even other animals for shelter and nesting.

Objective Students tell what animals eat for food and explain how a food chain connects living things.

Chapter 5 Lesson 3 20 min

What is a food chain?

1. Build Background

Standards Warm Up

Activate Prior Knowledge Have children name things that they might eat for dinner. List the foods in two columns labeled *Foods from Plants* and *Foods from Animals*.

2. Teach

Science Study Notebook

 Printable Lesson Study Guide
Have children check their understanding of Lesson 3 by completing p. 66 as they read.

Share and Talk

Read pp. 138–139 with children. Review how the plant gets food. Ask what kind of animal eats the plant.

Scaffolded Questions

Use the following guiding questions to monitor children's comprehension.

1. **Explain** What is the animal eating for food on p. 138? *The caterpillar is eating a leaf.*

2. **Interpret** How are the plant and animals connected in the food chain? *The animals eat the plant for food, and other animals eat the animals for food.*

3. **Judge** Do you think more animals might be in this food chain? Explain. *Possible answer: Yes. A bigger animal can eat the bird.*

Extend Science Vocabulary

▶ Discuss how a chain is made of connected links. Then explain that the plants and animals in a **food chain** are connected or linked as well.

▶ Ask children to represent the parts of the food chain on pp. 138–139 by linking arms. Have the first child say, "I am a plant; a plant makes its own food." Children who follow can tell what animal they are and what they eat.

Lesson 3

What is a food chain?

You know plants use energy from sunlight to make food.
You know some animals eat plants.
2 Then other animals eat those animals.
This is called a **food chain.**
Look at one kind of food chain.

This plant uses sunlight to make food. A caterpillar eats the leaf for food.

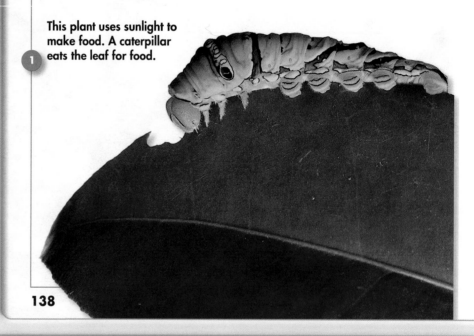

138

Big Idea	**Teacher Background**
Food chains link many different animals living in a shared environment.	▶ The animals in any food chain share at least part of an environment. For example, a bald eagle's environment includes both the places where its food lives (in the water or on the ground) and the places where it makes its nest (high up on rocks or in trees).
	▶ People share many environments with animals. People can eat both plants and animals and are at the top of some food chains. For example, chickens eat grain (from plants). People eat chickens or the eggs chickens produce.
	Common Misconception Children might think that larger animals are always higher on the food chain than smaller animals. Point out that some very large animals, such as elephants, eat only plants. A cow is a large animal but eats only grasses and grains.

Plants and animals depend on each other through food chains.

✔Lesson Review

1. What do animals eat for food?
   1. Animals eat plants or other animals for food.

2. **Predict** What might eat the bird?
   2. Possible answer: A larger animal might eat a bird.

Yum!
The bird eats the caterpillar for food.

keyword: foodchains
code: gr1p138

139

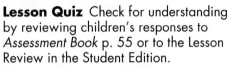

▶ **Active Glossary** Children who need more practice with vocabulary terms may review vocabulary online or use vocabulary cards (*Science Study Notebook*, pp. 59–60).

▶ **SciLinks** Children can go online to discover more about *food chains* by using the NSTA SciLink available at **www.sfsuccessnet.com** (keyword: **food chains** code: **gr1p138**).

3. Summarize and Assess

➡ QUICK Summary

▶ Animals eat plants or other animals for food.

▶ All plants and animals are connected and depend upon each other through food chains.

Assess
Printable Resources

Lesson Quiz Check for understanding by reviewing children's responses to *Assessment Book* p. 55 or to the Lesson Review in the Student Edition.

Intervention Study Guide Use pp. 40–41 to review and reinforce lesson concepts as needed.

Universal Access

English Learners
Explain a Food Chain Write the words *food chain, plant, animal,* and *eats* on the board. Model the words using the food chain pictured on pp. 138–139. Encourage volunteers to model the words also.

LSB2 ELD Listening and Speaking
Beginning Help children to identify the plant and animals in the food chain. Have volunteers point to and name each part of the food chain when responding to these questions: What makes its own food? (A plant) What eats the plant? (A caterpillar) What eats the caterpillar? (A bird)

LSE12 ELD Listening and Speaking
Intermediate Model these sentences that describe the food chain. *First, the ___ makes its own food. Next, the ___ eats the ___. Then, the ___ eats the ___.* Have children complete the sentences aloud and describe the food chain to a partner.

REA13 ELD Reading
Advanced Have children look at a food chain with a partner and identify its beginning, middle, and end. Have them point to the parts of the food chain as they discuss it.

Advanced Learners
Identify a Food Chain Ask children to suggest an example of a different food chain. Let them draw and write a caption for each link in the food chain. Volunteers can present their food chains to the class, describing what each living thing eats for food.

Extra Support
Make a Food "Chain" Review the definition of *food chain* and write the term on the board. Then, give each child several long strips of paper wide enough for the child to draw a plant or animal from a food chain on each strip. Show them how to use glue to link their pictures into a chain in order. Then, ask them to describe their food "chains."

Special Needs
Pictures of Animals Eating Have children draw or find pictures of an animal that eats plants for food. Then have children draw or find a picture of an animal that eats other animals for food. Allow them to share their pictures with the class.

1LS2.c **Life Sciences** Students know animals eat plants or other animals for food and may also use plants or even other animals for shelter and nesting.

Objectives

▶ Students tell what animals in a desert might eat.

▶ Students describe a desert food chain.

Chapter 5   Lesson 4   30 min

How do living things get food in a desert?

1. Build Background

Standards Warm Up

Activate Prior Knowledge Show children pictures of some animals that live in a desert. Ask children to tell what these desert animals might eat. Write their suggestions on the board and then review them at the end of the lesson.

2. Teach

⇘ *QUICK* Plan

▶ As a class, take a picture walk through the lesson to discuss visuals and captions.

▶ **AudioText** Use the audio version of the Student Edition at a technology center.

▶ Encourage children to work in teams to answer lesson questions.

Science Study Notebook

 **Printable Lesson Study Guide**
Have children check their understanding of Lesson 4 by completing p. 67 as they read.

Lesson 4

How do living things get food in a desert?

You know that a desert is an environment. There are food chains in a desert. Desert plants use energy from sunlight to make food.

2 Some insects eat the plants for food.

This shrub grows in the desert.

140

 Crunch!
The insect eats the leaves of the desert shrub.

1

Big Idea	**Teacher Background**
Desert plants and animals are part of a food chain.	▶ The food chain on pp. 140–143 is one example of a food chain in the desert. Another desert food chain could show a roadrunner eating a scorpion and a hawk eating the roadrunner. There are many desert food chains that contain a roadrunner. Food webs show many different types of food chains and how these various food chains overlap in an environment. **Common Misconception** Children might think that an animal will die if its usual food source disappears. But in reality many animals eat a variety of foods; therefore, if one type of food is unavailable, the animal might find another type of food to eat and will survive.

The lizard sees the insect.
The hungry lizard eats
the insect for food.

Zap!
The lizard will
catch the insect.

1. ✓Checkpoint What does the lizard
eat for food? 1. The lizard eats insects for food.

2. What might an animal in a desert eat?
   2. Answers may vary. Possible answer: An animal in the desert might eat plants or other animals.

141

Universal Access

English Learners
Put a Food Chain in Order Review the names of the desert plants and animals using the small images on p. 143. Identify each plant or animal and have children repeat each name after you.

LSB2 ELD Listening and Speaking
Beginning Model the sequence of the food chain by asking questions such as: "What comes first in this food chain? What comes second?" Review the sequence with children.

RET4 ELD Reading
Intermediate Write the words *plant, insect, lizard, roadrunner,* and *coyote* on separate note cards. Read the words. Give a set of note cards to each pair of children. Let one child put the cards in order and the other check the sequence.

WEA3 ELD Writing
Advanced On the board, draw five large boxes connected by arrows and label them 1–5. Have children work in pairs to copy the boxes. Then have them write in the first box what happens first in the desert food chain. (The plant takes in sunlight.) Have them fill in the other boxes.

Mathematics Support
1NS1.2 Number Sense

Have children count how many plants and animals are in each food chain in Lesson 3 and on p. 143. Then have children compare the number of plants and animals in each food chain using a symbol for less than or greater than. (3 < 5, 5 > 3)

Scaffolded Questions

Use the following guiding questions to monitor children's comprehension.

1 **Tell** What eats the desert plants? The insect eats the desert plants.

2 **Explain** Why is the plant at the bottom of this food chain? It uses energy from sunlight to make its own food and is the first thing to be eaten in this food chain.

3 **Compare** How is the food chain on pp. 140–141 the same as the food chain in Lesson 3? Possible answer: Both begin with sunlight. Both food chains include insects eating plants and larger animals eating insects.

Extend Science Vocabulary

▶ Show children pictures of other plants and animals that live in a desert.

▶ Make a word web on the board with the word *desert* at the center.

▶ Encourage children to add words to the web that name the desert animals. Point out that each plant and animal in the web is part of one or more food chains.

Diagnostic Check

If . . . children are having difficulty understanding how desert plants and animals meet their energy requirements through food chains,

then . . . have them trace the direction of the food chain on p. 143 by putting their finger on the desert bush and following the arrows up from the insect to the coyote.

2. Teach CONTINUED

Share and Talk

Remind children that all living things need food. Discuss how the living things in the desert get food. Help children to understand how the coyote is connected to the desert bush through a food chain.

Active Art Children can explore an interactive version of a desert food chain on pp. 142–143 by using Active Art at **www.sfsuccessnet.com**.

Write About Science

1WOL1.1 **Written and Oral English Language Conventions** Have children write sentences about a desert food chain. Provide children with sentence starters such as:

First, the ___ eats the ___.

Next, the ___ eats the ___.

Then the ___ eats the ___.

Encourage children to add other sentences if they wish.

Writing Rubric

4	The sentences are detailed and complete. The written piece includes three or more sentences describing a desert food chain. There are few or no errors.
3	The sentences are detailed and complete. The written piece includes at least two sentences describing a desert food chain. There are some errors.
2	The sentences are incomplete and do not fully describe a desert food chain. There are many errors.
1	The sentences are incomplete and do not accurately describe a desert food chain. There are many errors that make the writing difficult to understand.

Tip

If children have difficulty putting events in order when writing, model how to draw diagrams of food chains before they begin. Explain how to draw the animals and plants in the food chains and to show the order with arrows. Encourage children to use their diagrams to help them write.

Food for Desert Animals

The roadrunner sees the lizard.

1 The roadrunner eats the lizard for food.

The coyote sees the roadrunner.

2 The coyote eats the roadrunner for food.

Gulp!
The roadrunner will eat the lizard.

Look for Active Art animations at www.sfsuccessnet.com

142

Universal Access

Special Needs

Draw an Animal and Its Food Have children with hearing impairments fold a sheet of drawing paper in half vertically. On the right, have them draw an animal that is part of a food chain. On the left, have children draw a plant or animal that the animal eats. Children should label their pictures *Food* and *Animal* and then share their pictures with the class.

Advanced Learners

Sing a Food Chain Song Encourage children to help write a food chain song sung to the tune of "The Farmer in the Dell." Start off by writing and singing this verse:

The plant makes its food.
The plant makes its food.
Hi, ho, the derry-o,
The plant makes its food.

Have children work with a partner to write verses about the insect, the lizard, the roadrunner, and the coyote. Each verse should tell what the animal eats. (The ___ eats the ___ .) After the children have written their verses, have them sing the song to the class.

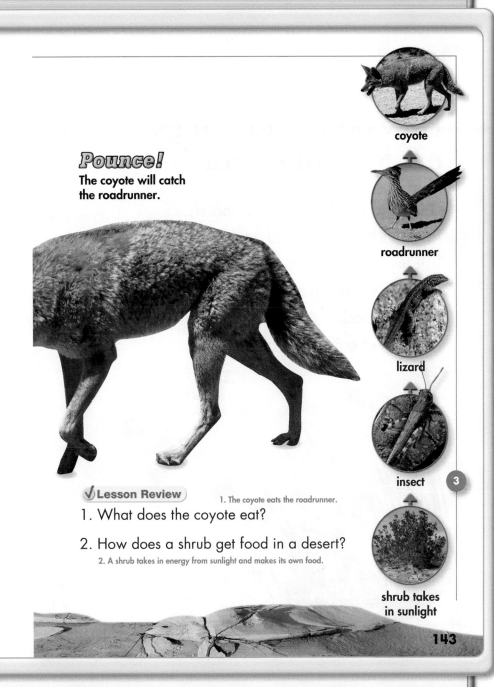

Pounce!

The coyote will catch the roadrunner.

coyote

roadrunner

lizard

insect

3

shrub takes in sunlight

✓ **Lesson Review**

1. The coyote eats the roadrunner.

1. What does the coyote eat?

2. How does a shrub get food in a desert?

2. A shrub takes in energy from sunlight and makes its own food.

143

Universal Access

Extra Support
Make a Desert Mural Have children work together to make a mural of a desert that includes the plants and animals from the food chain. Give each child the chance to tell how living things are connected using the mural as a point of reference. Have children work together to come up with a title for the mural.

Use the following guiding questions to monitor children's comprehension.

1 **Name** What does the roadrunner eat? The roadrunner eats the lizard.

2 **Interpret** Does the coyote eat a plant or another animal? The coyote eats another animal.

3 **Hypothesize** What might happen to the insect if the plants in the desert died? The insect might not be able to find the food it needs to live.

Extend Science Vocabulary

▶ Have children find the roadrunner on p. 142. Ask them why they think this bird is called a roadrunner. (Possible answer: It runs.)

▶ Tell children that the roadrunner does run and walk more than it flies. Have children identify situations when the bird might run. (Possible answers: When it is being chased by a coyote; when it is trying to catch a lizard)

▶ Explain to children that a roadrunner can run very fast. Tell them that it can fly, but only for short spurts.

3. Summarize and Assess

⇒ *QUICK* Summary

▶ Desert animals eat plants and other animals.

▶ In a desert, plants use energy from sunlight to make food, insects eat the plants, the lizard eats insects, the roadrunner eats the lizard, and the coyote eats the roadrunner.

Assess
 Printable Resources

Lesson Quiz Check for understanding by reviewing children's responses to *Assessment Book* p. 56 or to the Lesson Review in the Student Edition.

Intervention Study Guide Use pp. 42–43 to review and reinforce lesson concepts as needed.

Life Sciences Students know animals eat plants or other animals for food and may also use plants or even other animals for shelter and nesting.

Objectives

▶ Students tell what animals in a marsh might eat.

▶ Students describe a marsh food chain.

Chapter 5   Lesson 5   30 min

How do living things get food in a marsh?

1. Build Background

Standards Warm Up

Activate Prior Knowledge Bring in pictures of wetland areas, such as marshes, bogs, swamps, and everglades. Have children describe the pictures. Use their descriptions to elicit the word *wetland*. Ask volunteers who have visited a wetland to describe it.

2. Teach

▷ QUICK Plan

▶ As a class, take a picture walk through the lesson to discuss visuals and captions.

▶ **AudioText** Use the audio version of the Student Edition at a technology center.

▶ Encourage children to work in teams to answer lesson questions.

Science Study Notebook

Printable Lesson Study Guide
Have children check their understanding of Lesson 5 by completing p. 68 as they read.

Lesson 5

How do living things get food in a marsh?

There are food chains in a marsh.

1 A **marsh** is a wetland environment. Tall grass grows in a marsh. The grass uses energy from sunlight to make food. The cricket eats the grass for food.

Snap!
The cricket bites the grass.

2

144

Big Idea	**Teacher Background**
The size of plant and animal populations impacts food chains.	▶ When the number of plants and animals in an environment changes, food chains are impacted. For example, frogs in an area could decline due to pollution or development. If there are not enough frogs to eat, the snake population will decline. When the snake population declines, the frog population has time to grow. The change in the snake and frog population will also affect the hawk and cricket populations.

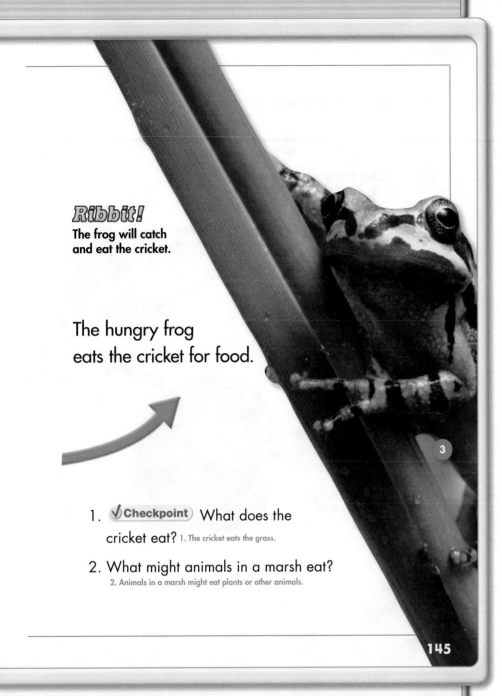

Ribbit!
The frog will catch
and eat the cricket.

The hungry frog
eats the cricket for food.

1. ✓Checkpoint What does the
cricket eat? 1. The cricket eats the grass.

2. What might animals in a marsh eat?
2. Animals in a marsh might eat plants or other animals.

145

Universal Access

English Learners
Marsh Food Chains Write the word *marsh* on the board. Remind children that a marsh is a wetland. Have children draw a picture of a sunny marsh that contains water, long grass, a cricket, and a frog.

LSB2 ELD Listening and Speaking
Beginning Write the following sentence frames: *This wetland is called a ___. The cricket lives in the ___. The frog lives in the ___.* Help children choose a word that completes each sentence. Then model how to read the sentences aloud.

LS12 ELD Listening and Speaking
Intermediate Have children make stick puppets of the grass, the cricket, and the frog. Have partners use their puppets to demonstrate how the cricket eats the grass, and the frog eats the cricket.

WEA3 ELD Writing
Advanced Provide these sentence frames: *The marsh has food for plants and ___. The grass uses ___ to make food. The ___ eats the grass. The ___ eats the cricket.* Then have children complete and read each sentence.

English-Language Arts Support
1RC2.7 Reading Comprehension
▶ Read pp.144–145 with children.
▶ Ask children how the tall grasses in the marsh get food. (Grasses use energy from sunlight to make food.)
▶ Ask children what the cricket eats (grass). Ask what the frog eats (the cricket).

Use the following guiding questions to monitor children's comprehension.

1 Recall What is a marsh? A marsh is a wetland environment.

2 Sequence What eats the plant and is food for the frog? The cricket eats the plant and is food for the frog.

3 Contrast How is the frog different from the cricket? The frog eats animals for food, and the cricket eats plants for food.

Extend Science Vocabulary

▶ Explain that a **marsh** is one kind of wetland. Tell children that marshes contain soft land, which may be partly covered by either salt water or fresh water. Plants and grasses grow there, but not many trees do.

▶ Ask children to brainstorm words that would describe a place that is soaked with water *(soggy, squishy, wet, moist)*. You may have children feel a sponge soaked with water to facilitate their descriptions.

▶ **DIGITAL 9 Active Glossary** Children who need more practice with vocabulary terms may review vocabulary online or use vocabulary cards (*Science Study Notebook*, pp. 59–60).

Diagnostic Check

If . . . children have difficulty understanding how marsh plants and animals meet their energy requirements through food chains,

then . . . have them put their finger on the grass and trace the arrows to the cricket and the frog as they listen to the description of the food chain being read again.

2. Teach CONTINUED

Share and Talk

Read aloud pp. 146–147. Review with children the definition of a food chain (the way food passes from one living thing to another). Discuss the different plants and animals this food chain in the marsh connects (plant, cricket, frog, snake, hawk).

Write About Science

1WS1.1 Writing Strategies Have children write two sentences about one of the marsh animals in the food chain. Ask them to tell what it eats and what eats it.

Writing Rubric

4	The child's writing focuses on one marsh animal. The written piece includes two sentences that tell what the selected animal eats and what eats it. There are few or no mistakes.
3	The child's writing focuses on marsh animals. The written piece includes two sentences that tell what the animals eat and what eats them. There are some mistakes.
2	The child's writing lacks focus. The written piece includes one or two sentences about what animals eat. There are many mistakes.
1	The child's writing lacks focus. The writing does not tell what a marsh animal eats or what eats it. There are many mistakes that make it difficult to understand.

Tip

Printable Graphic Organizer Use *Graphic Organizer 2* (TE p. EMxx) with children to help them understand the sequence of "who eats whom" in the marsh. Have children fill in the middle box of the sequence with the animal they selected. Direct them to draw in the first box what the selected animal eats, and to draw in the last box what, if anything, eats it. Then model how to use the graphic organizer to help write sentences.

Food for Marsh Animals

The hungry snake sees the frog.
The snake moves toward the frog.

Gulp!
1 The snake will eat the frog.

146

Universal Access

Special Needs

Sequencing a Food Chain Write the following words in random order on the board: *grass, cricket, frog, snake, hawk.* Have children take turns starting a food chain by writing the word *grass* and numbering it "1." Then have children continue until the numbered food chain is complete. Have them read the list together.

Advanced Learners

Marsh Research Project Help children use the library media center to find additional information about a marsh. Encourage them to look for other marsh animals to add to the food chain or to a food web. Ask them to share their findings with the class.

The hungry hawk
sees the snake.
The hawk flies
toward the snake.

hawk

snake

Swoop!
The hawk will
catch the snake
2 and eat it.

frog

✓**Lesson Review**

1. The frog eats the cricket.

1. What does the frog eat?

cricket

2. Predict What might happen if there
were no plants living in the marsh?

2. Answers will vary. Possible answer: There would be no
animals living in the marsh.

plants take
in sunlight

147

Universal Access

Extra Support
Make a Book Help children fold two sheets of paper in half to
make a book. Ask children to think about their favorite marsh animal
and to think of a story about how that animal gets food. Children
can either draw pictures or write simple sentences with your help.
Remind children to write the title of the story on the cover. Then let
children share their stories with the class.

Scaffolded Questions

Use the following guiding questions to monitor children's
comprehension.

1 **Tell** What does the snake eat? The snake eats the
frog.

2 **Describe** How does the hawk get food? It catches
the snake and eats it.

3 **Infer** Why is the Sun so important to the food chain?
Plants must have sunlight in order to make their own
food. The animals that eat plants are food for other
animals.

Extend Science Vocabulary

▶ Write the words *cricket, frog, snake,* and *hawk* on the
board.

▶ As a class, discuss how each animal moves. (The cricket
crawls, hops, and jumps; the frog jumps and hops; the
snake slithers; the hawk flies and soars.) List the action
words.

▶ Ask volunteers to use the action words in sentences that
describe the movement of the marsh animals.

3. Summarize and Assess

⇒ QUICK Summary

▶ Marsh animals eat plants and other animals.

▶ In a marsh, plants use energy from sunlight to make
food, the cricket eats the plants, the frog eats the
cricket, the snake eats the frog, and the hawk eats the
snake.

Assess

 Printable Resources

Lesson Quiz Check for understanding
by reviewing children's responses to
Assessment Book p. 57 or to the Lesson
Review in the Student Edition.

Intervention Study Guide Use pp. 44–45 to
review and reinforce lesson concepts as needed.

California Science
CONTENT STANDARDS FOCUS

 Life Sciences Students know how to infer what animals eat from the shape of their teeth (e.g., sharp teeth: eats meat; flat teeth: eats plants).

Objectives

▶ Students identify which animals eat animals for food and describe the shape of their teeth.

▶ Students identify which animals eat plants for food and describe the shape of their teeth.

Chapter 5   Lesson 6   30 min

What do animals eat?

1. Build Background

Standards Warm Up

Activate Prior Knowledge Give children mirrors so they can look at their teeth. Ask them if they can find both sharp teeth and flat teeth in their mouth. Have them describe their teeth. List the descriptive words on the board.

2. Teach

⇒ QUICK Plan

▶ As a class, take a picture walk through the lesson to discuss visuals and captions.

▶ **AudioText** Use the audio version of the Student Edition at a technology center.

▶ Encourage children to work in teams to answer lesson questions.

Science Study Notebook

 **Printable Lesson Study Guide**
Have children check their understanding of Lesson 6 by completing p. 69 as they read.

Lesson 6

What do animals eat?

Some animals eat other animals.
Wolves and crocodiles eat other animals.
Lions eat other animals too.

This is the skull of a lion. Look at the sharp, pointed teeth.

This lion is chasing another animal to eat.

148

Big Ideas	**Teacher Background**
Different animals depend on different sources of food.	▶ Some animals eat mainly plants. These animals are called herbivores.
	▶ Some animals eat mainly other animals. These animals are called carnivores.
	▶ Other animals eat both plants and animals. These animals are called omnivores.
You can infer what animals eat from the shape of their teeth.	▶ Many animals that eat mainly plants have flat teeth.
	▶ Many animals that eat mainly animals have sharp, pointed teeth.

A lion has sharp, pointed teeth. Sharp, pointed teeth can rip and tear meat.

How can you tell what animals eat?
You can look at their teeth.
Many animals that eat other animals have sharp, pointed teeth.

1. ✓Checkpoint What do lions eat for food?
   1. Lions eat other animals for food.

2. ✎Writing in Science How can you tell what lions eat? 2. You can look at their teeth.

149

Universal Access

English Learners
Animals' Teeth and What They Eat Write the words *flat teeth* and *sharp teeth* on the board. Ask children to name animals that would go under each heading.

LSB2 **ELD Listening and Speaking**
Beginning Have children point to pictures of animals that show their teeth. Ask, "Does this animal have flat or pointed teeth?" Write the animal's name under the right heading. Read it aloud; have children repeat.

REI11 **ELD Reading**
Intermediate Give children pictures of animals' teeth. Have them infer whether the animals eat plants or other animals, and record their inferences on a Venn diagram. If an animal eats both plants and animals, they can write its name in the middle section.

RA6 **ELD Reading**
Advanced Have partners read and observe animals in a book such as *What Do You Do When Something Wants to Eat You?* by Steve Jenkins (ISBN: 0-618-15243-1). After reading, have them make posters of what the animals eat and their teeth.

English-Language Arts Support
1RC2.7 **Reading Comprehension**

▶ After reading pp. 148–149 aloud, have children suggest what the main ideas of the pages are.

▶ Ask children to choose the ideas that they think best tell what the pages are about. Record the main ideas on the board.

Scaffolded Questions
Use the following guiding questions to monitor children's comprehension.

1 **Recall** What is one way you can tell what an animal eats? You can look at the animal's teeth.

2 **Infer** Crocodiles eat other animals. What type of teeth do you think crocodiles have? Explain your reasoning. Possible answer: Crocodiles eat other animals, so they probably have sharp teeth.

3 **Apply** If an animal has both flat and sharp teeth, what do you think it eats? Possible answer: The animal might eat both plants and animals.

Extend Science Vocabulary

▶ Write the word *sharp* on the board. Make a list of things that are sharp (teeth, corners, sharpened pencils, rocks, pins, scissors).

▶ Write the following sentence on the board: *Teeth are sharp.* Then invite children to discuss the meaning of the word *sharp* in the sentence and whether some teeth are sharper than other teeth.

Diagnostic Check

If . . . children are having a hard time understanding how sharp, pointed teeth help lions eat other animals,

then . . . show them a fork with sharp, pointy tines. Explain to them that the lions' sharp teeth are like the tines used for picking up and tearing food.

Share and Talk

Have children point to the picture of the cow's skull. Have them trace along the top of the teeth with their fingers. Then have them feel their own flat teeth with their fingers. Point out that the cow's teeth are flat. They do not go up and down like the lion's teeth do.

Ask: Why don't cows need sharp, pointed teeth? Because they eat plants, not other animals

Write About Science

1WA2.2 **Writing Applications** Have children use what they know about teeth to write one or two sentences that describe cows' teeth and explain how they are used.

Writing Rubric

4	The child's sentences are complete and clearly describe cows' teeth and how they are used. The writer includes many relevant details. There are very few errors.
3	The child's sentences are complete and describe cows' teeth and how they are used. The writer includes some details. There are some errors.
2	The child's sentences are incomplete and give an incomplete description of cows' teeth and how they are used. The writer includes few relevant details. There are many errors.
1	The child's sentences are incomplete and do not describe cows' teeth or how they are used. The writer uses no relevant details. There are many errors that make the writing difficult to understand.

Tip

Help children think of words that can describe cows' teeth. List the words on the board. Model how children can use the words to write their sentences.

Animals that Eat Plants

Many animals eat plants for food.
Deer and squirrels eat plants.
Cows eat plants too.

Crunch!
This cow eats grass.

150

Universal Access

Special Needs
Make a Model of Teeth Give children a piece of construction paper. Ask them to make a model of either a lion's teeth or a cow's teeth. After they make the models, have them take turns gently touching and tracing other children's models. Have children infer what type of food an animal with pointed or flat teeth might eat.

Advanced Learners
Which Teeth Are Used for What Have children look at the teeth in their mouth. Have them count and record how many of their teeth have flat surfaces and how many have pointed surfaces. Have children use what they know to determine which teeth are used when eating different types of food. Have children share their findings and ideas with the class.

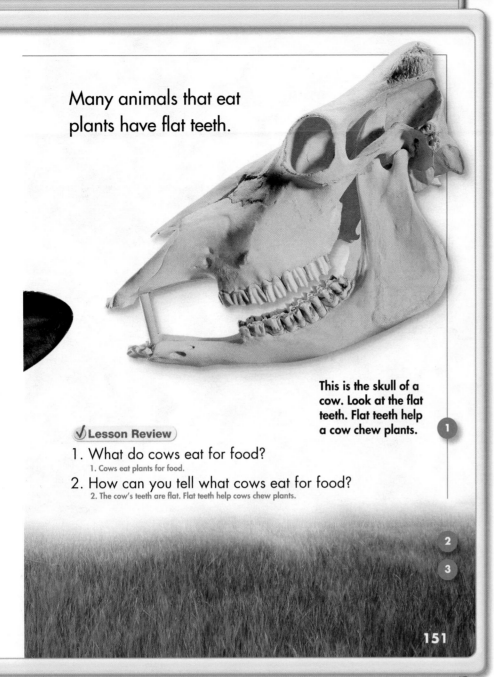

Many animals that eat plants have flat teeth.

This is the skull of a cow. Look at the flat teeth. Flat teeth help a cow chew plants.

✓ Lesson Review

1. What do cows eat for food?
   1. Cows eat plants for food.

2. How can you tell what cows eat for food?
   2. The cow's teeth are flat. Flat teeth help cows chew plants.

151

Universal Access

Extra Support
Observe Teeth Have children look through magazines and books to find pictures of different animals showing their teeth. Have children describe the shape of the teeth as pointed or flat. After they describe the shape, help them to determine whether the animal eats animals or plants.

Use the following guiding questions to monitor children's comprehension.

1 **Recognize** Does the cow have pointed or flat teeth? The cow has flat teeth.

2 **Compare** What is the difference between cows' teeth and lions' teeth? Cows' teeth are flat, and lions' teeth are pointed.

3 **Judge** Could a cow easily eat another animal? Possible answer: No, because it does not have pointed teeth to help it tear the meat.

Extend Science Vocabulary

▶ Write the phrase *flat teeth* on the board. Ask children to describe what it means.

▶ Have children find flat surfaces in the classroom and then tell about them in sentences such as "The top of my desk is flat."

▶ Discuss with children the meaning of the word *chew*. Ask children for words that have a similar meaning *(grind, crush)*. Have children describe the motion of their flat teeth when they chew.

3. Summarize and Assess

⟫ *QUICK* Summary

▶ Some animals that eat other animals have sharp teeth.

▶ Some animals that eat plants have flat teeth.

▶ Animals eat plants and other animals.

Assess
📠 Printable Resources

Lesson Quiz Check for understanding by reviewing children's responses to *Assessment Book* p. 58 or to the Lesson Review in the Student Edition.

Intervention Study Guide Use pp. 46–47 to review and reinforce lesson concepts as needed.

California
CONTENT STANDARDS FOCUS

1PS1.1 **Statistics, Data Analysis, and Probability** Sort objects by common attributes and describe the categories.

1IE4.b **Investigation and Experimentation** Record observations and data with pictures, numbers, or written statements.

Objective Students use a Venn diagram to sort animals by what they eat.

Math in Science 25 min

1. Build Background

Warm Up
Activate Prior Knowledge

▶ Invite children to name animals that live on land and animals that live in water.

▶ Ask children if some of the animals they name live both on land and in water (e.g., turtles, frogs, sea otters). Show children how a Venn diagram can be used to sort these animals.

2. Teach

Sort Objects

Have children look at the Venn diagram on p. 153.

Ask: What does the overlapping part of the two circles mean? It means that an animal eats both plants and animals.

Help children see that the overlapping circles show where the two sets or groups have something in common.

Share and Talk

Have children work in pairs to answer the questions on p. 153. Encourage them to discuss how they grouped the animals in the Venn diagram by the kinds of food the animal eats.

eTools Use the Geometry Shapes Tool to practice sorting objects by a common attribute. Create a set of shapes. Then have children sort them by their shapes. You can change the colors of the shapes to sort them by a shape and a color.

Math in Science

Grouping Animals

Look at the Venn diagram.
It groups animals by what they eat.

152

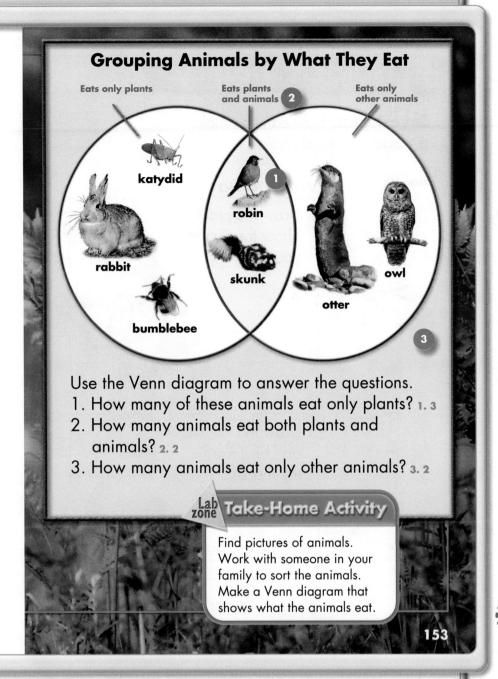

Grouping Animals by What They Eat

Eats only plants

Eats plants and animals ②

Eats only other animals

katydid

robin ①

rabbit

skunk

bumblebee

otter

owl

③

Use the Venn diagram to answer the questions.
1. How many of these animals eat only plants? 1. 3
2. How many animals eat both plants and animals? 2. 2
3. How many animals eat only other animals? 3. 2

Lab zone Take-Home Activity

Find pictures of animals. Work with someone in your family to sort the animals. Make a Venn diagram that shows what the animals eat.

153

Take-Home Activity

Tips for Success

▶ Some children may find many pictures of animals but not be able to fit them all on the Venn diagram.

▶ You may wish to allow children to name, rather than picture, the animals they find.

Mathematics Support

1PS1.1 Statistics, Data Analysis, and Probability

Provide children with a blank Venn diagram. Then give them a set of objects, such a variety of buttons. Have the children sort the buttons into groups on the Venn diagram by their color, shape, size, or other attributes. Then have the children suggest how to label each circle of the diagram.

Scaffolded Questions

Use the following guiding questions to monitor children's comprehension.

① **Identify** What does the robin eat? It eats both plants and animals.

② **Apply** Bears like to eat berries and mice. In what part of the Venn diagram would you put a bear? The bear would be in the center section of the Venn diagram.

③ **Assemble** What is another way to group the animals on p. 153? Possible answer: Groups could be sorted by how they move around: fly or walk on legs.

3. Summarize and Assess

⇒ *QUICK* Summary

▶ You can group objects based on common characteristics or attributes.

▶ Venn diagrams can be used for sorting or grouping.

Assess

Check for understanding by reviewing responses to questions on p. 153. Children may explain that for each question they were careful to count only the animals that answered the question.

1LS2.c **Life Sciences** Students know animals eat plants or other animals for food and may also use plants or even other animals for shelter and nesting.

1IE4.a **Investigation and Experimentation** Draw pictures that portray some features of the thing being described. (Also **1IE4.b**)

Objective Students make a model of a marsh food chain.

Guided Inquiry

 20 min

1. Get Ready

Materials for Small Groups

4 *paper plates*   crayons or markers
2 *pieces of yarn*   masking tape

Materials listed in *italics* are kit materials.

Alternative Materials Sheets of white paper may be used in place of paper plates.

⤳ *QUICK* Plan

► Have children draw their animals on paper rather than paper plates to construct the food chain.

► This activity may be set up as a center activity.

2. What to Do

Preview

► **Active Glossary** Reinforce science vocabulary by encouraging children to use academic language from the chapter as they do the activity. For children who need extra support, post vocabulary cards (*Science Study Notebook*, pp. 59–60).

► Conduct an inventory of materials with children. For English Learners, solicit alternative names for items in their home language. Post the names of materials and other academic language, such as *model, food chain,* and *marsh,* on a word wall.

► You may wish to preview science content in Lesson 3.

Advance Preparation Cut two 4-foot lengths of yarn for each group.

Tips

► Help children understand that connecting the plates with yarn shows how plants and animals depend on each other through food chains.

► Discuss with children that the food chain begins with energy from sunlight, which the plants use to make food. Then animals eat food to meet their energy requirements.

Lab zone Guided Inquiry

Investigate How can you make a model of a food chain?

Materials

paper plates

crayons or markers

masking tape

yarn

Process Skills

Making a model can help you understand and explain ideas.

What to Do

1 Draw the plant. Show the Sun in your drawing.

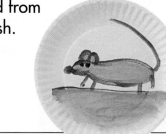

2 Draw the rat, snake, and bird from the marsh.

154

Digital Classroom

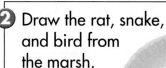 **Activity Video** Prepare for and rehearse the activity before class.

Printable Activity Rubric Monitor children's progress using the Activity Rubric located at **www.sfsuccessnet.com**.

Printable LabZone Activity Provide children with additional activities located at **www.sfsuccessnet.com**.

Call **1-888-537-4908** with activity questions.

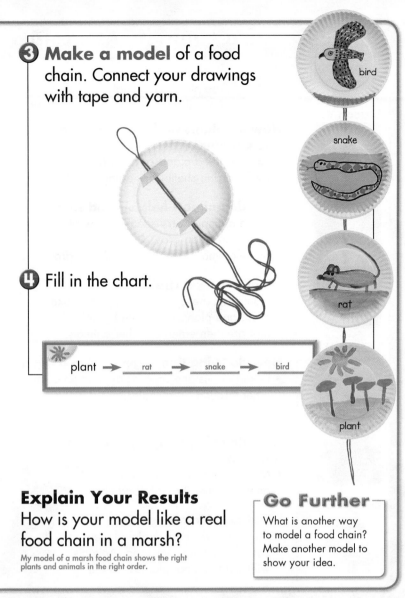

3 **Make a model** of a food chain. Connect your drawings with tape and yarn.

4 Fill in the chart.

plant → rat → snake → bird

Explain Your Results
How is your model like a real food chain in a marsh?

My model of a marsh food chain shows the right plants and animals in the right order.

Go Further

What is another way to model a food chain? Make another model to show your idea.

155

Big Idea

Animals eat plants or other animals in a food chain.

Teacher Background

▶ A food chain is the path of food energy from a consumer back to its original producer. However, in nature, most animals eat a variety of foods, creating a more complicated web of food relationships.

▶ Humans are at the top of a food chain.

Record Data After they have constructed the food chain model, have children fill in the chart. Each space should contain the name of the next animal in the chain. Explain to children that the arrows represent the transfer of energy.

Ask Questions Ask children what animals eat. What animals can they think of that eat plants? What animals eat other animals? What animals eat both plants and other animals? Where would people be found on a food chain?

3. Explain Your Results

Science Study Notebook

Printable Resources
Activity Recording Sheet
Discuss the results of the activity by reviewing completed pp. 70–71. Ask volunteers to explain how their models are like a real food chain. What does the model tell us about what the animals in the marsh eat?

Activity Rubric Use *Science Study Notebook Teacher's Guide* p. T29 to evaluate children's work.

Go Further

▶ Discuss other ways to model a food chain. Help children understand that the chart they completed to record data is also a model.

▶ Collect any other questions about food chains and post them on the bulletin board. Encourage children to investigate these questions on their own.

1. Lesson Summaries

▶ Review the lesson summaries on p. 156 by asking children each lesson focus question and encouraging them to answer using their own words. If children struggle to answer, have them look at the lesson pictures to review the concepts.

▶ Divide the class into six groups and assign each group one lesson from the chapter. Children should reread and review the material for their assigned lesson.

▶ Model a concept web and help each group use words and pictures to create a concept web for their assigned lesson.

2. Reinforce Concepts

▶ Have each group present its concept web to the class. Encourage groups to give details that show how the topics in their lesson relate to the chapter's Big Idea. Invite children to discuss the concept webs of the other groups.

▶ Suggest to children that they combine their concept webs to make a mural for the chapter.

▶ When the class mural is complete, children may use it to prepare for the Chapter 5 Review/Test (pp. 158–159).

Chapter 5 Reviewing Key Concepts

Focus on the BIG Idea

Animals eat plants or animals and may use plants or animals for shelter. Some animals may spread seeds of plants.

Lesson 1

How do plants and animals need one another?
• Animals need plants or other animals for food and shelter or nesting.

Lesson 2

How do animals help spread seeds?
• Some animals carry seeds to new places where they can grow.
• Some animals bury seeds and they grow.

Lesson 3

What is a food chain?
• Plants use energy from sunlight to make food, and plants are eaten by animals that are then eaten by other animals.

Lesson 4

How do living things get food in a desert?
• Desert plants and animals depend on each other through food chains.

Lesson 5

How do living things get food in a marsh?
• Marsh plants and animals depend on each other through food chains.

Lesson 6

What do animals eat?
• Animals with sharp, pointed teeth eat other animals for food. Animals with flat teeth eat plants for food.

156

Further Learning

▶ Help English learners express their understanding of the chapter content by having them include pictures in the circles of their concept webs.

▶ Encourage advanced learners to add extra circles to their concept webs to provide additional details about the lesson content.

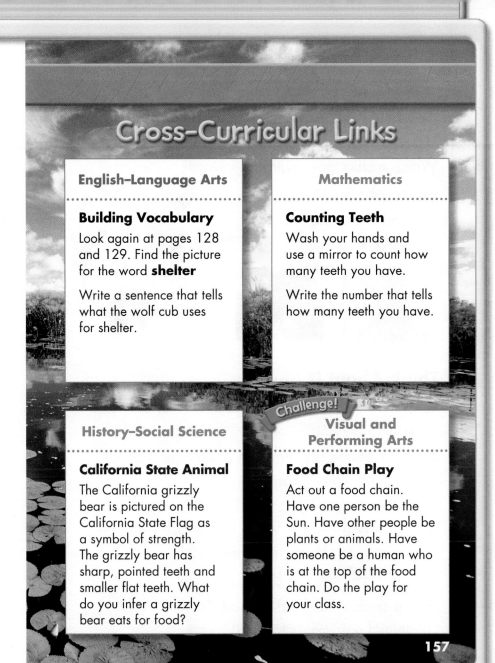

Cross-Curricular Links

English–Language Arts

Building Vocabulary

Look again at pages 128 and 129. Find the picture for the word **shelter**

Write a sentence that tells what the wolf cub uses for shelter.

Mathematics

Counting Teeth

Wash your hands and use a mirror to count how many teeth you have.

Write the number that tells how many teeth you have.

History–Social Science

California State Animal

The California grizzly bear is pictured on the California State Flag as a symbol of strength. The grizzly bear has sharp, pointed teeth and smaller flat teeth. What do you infer a grizzly bear eats for food?

Challenge!

Visual and Performing Arts

Food Chain Play

Act out a food chain. Have one person be the Sun. Have other people be plants or animals. Have someone be a human who is at the top of the food chain. Do the play for your class.

157

▶ Direct children's attention to the Big Idea on p. 156. Have children give an oral summary about the Big Idea. Encourage children to use vocabulary terms and other academic language from the chapter. Answers will vary but should include vocabulary terms.

Ask:

▶ Why are plants important to food chains? Most food chains begin with plants. Smaller animals on the food chain survive by eating plants.

▶ How do the teeth of humans show that humans eat both plants and animals? Humans have both sharp teeth for tearing meat and flat teeth for chewing plants.

Cross-Curricular Links

English-Language Arts
Building Vocabulary

1WOL1.1 **Written and Oral English Language Conventions** Answers will vary. See the Writing Rubric for Building Vocabulary to the right for support on scoring children's sentence.

Mathematics
Counting Teeth
1NS1.1 **Number Sense** Accept all reasonable answers.

History-Social Science
California State Animal
The grizzly bear eats both plants and animals.

Visual and Performing Arts
Challenge Food Chain Play
Check to see that children connect the theatrical concept of beginning, middle, and end to the flow of energy through a food chain.

Writing Rubric for Building Vocabulary

4	Child writes a clear, focused sentence that accurately states what wolf cubs use for shelter. Capitalization and punctuation are correct.
3	Child writes a simple sentence that states what wolf cubs use for shelter. The sentence may have errors in capitalization or end mark.
2	Child writes a sentence that is only partly accurate. The sentence may have errors in both capitalization and end mark.
1	Child writes a sentence that is unclear and does not answer the question. There are many errors.

Vocabulary

1. B

2. C

3. A

Think About It

4. Animals use plants and other animals for food and shelter.

5. Animals that eat other animals have sharp and pointed teeth.

6. Possible answer: Squirrels might use trees as shelter.

7. **Observe** This animal ate plants.

Refer to side columns for answers.

Chapter 5 Review/Test

Vocabulary
Which picture goes with each word?

1. shelter (page 134)

2. food chain (page 138)

3. marsh (page 144)

Think About It

4. How do animals use plants and other animals? (pages 133–135)

5. What shape are the teeth of animals that eat other animals? (pages 148–149)

6. ✏️ *Writing in Science* Write a sentence. Tell how squirrels might use trees. (page 134)

7. *Process Skills* **Observe** Look at the skull. What kind of food did this animal eat? (pages 150–151)

158

Universal Access

Special Needs
Accommodate individual children as needed to distinguish between lack of content knowledge and physical or linguistic limitations.

Common Accommodations
▶ Provide additional time.

▶ 🔊 **AudioText** Read the test. An audio recording of the Chapter Review/Test is available on AudioText.

▶ Allow children who have difficulty writing to audio record answers.

Assessment Resources

 Printable Chapter Test
Assessment Book pp. 63–66

 Success Tracker
Use this flexible, online assessment system to track Adequate Yearly Progress and provide intervention. Find it at **www.sfsuccessnet.com**.

 Printable Student Progress Report
TE pp. EMxvii–EMxviii

 Show What You Know
TE pp. 166–167

 ExamView
Customizable Chapter 5 Test

 MindPoint QuizShow
Chapter 5 review in game format

8. Possible answer:

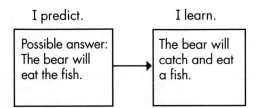

I predict.   I learn.

Possible answer: The bear will eat the fish. → The bear will catch and eat a fish.

California Standards Practice

9. D

10. A

---

8. **Predict** Tell what you think will happen. Read the story to find out. (page 138)

I predict.   I learn.

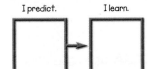

This bear will catch and eat a fish for food.

California Standards Practice

9. **Which uses other animals for nesting?**

   A bird

   B wolf

   C sea otter

   D flea

10. **Look at the pictures of the animals. Which does not fit in a marsh food chain?**

   A roadrunner

   B frog

   C snake

   D hawk

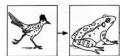

159

Intervention and Reteaching

California Science CONTENT STANDARDS FOCUS	Review Items	Student Edition	Teacher's Edition Resources			Ancillary Resources	
			Scaffolded Questions	Extend Vocab	Diagnostic Check	Intervention Study Guide	Science Study Notebook
1LS2.c Life Sciences Students know animals eat plants or other animals for food and may also use plants or even other animals for shelter and nesting.	1–4, 6, 8–10	128–147	133, 135, 136, 138, 141, 143, 145, 147	133, 135, 137, 138, 141, 143, 145, 147	133, 141, 145	36–45	57–60, 62, 64–68
1LS2.d Life Sciences Students know how to infer what animals eat from the shapes of their teeth (e.g., sharp teeth: eats meat; flat teeth: eats plants).	5, 7	148–151	149, 151	149, 151	149	46–47	57–60, 69

CONTENT STANDARDS FOCUS

1LS2.c **Life Sciences** Students know animals eat plants or other animals for food and may also use plants or even other animals for shelter and nesting.

1RW1.16 **Word Analysis, Fluency, and Systematic Vocabulary Development** Read aloud with fluency in a manner that sounds like natural speech.

Objective Students read and discuss how scientists use information gathered by satellites to understand how penguin populations in Antarctica change.

NASA 25 min

1. Build Background

Warm Up
Activate Prior Knowledge
▶ Ask children to tell what they know about penguins. Then ask them if they know what a satellite is.

▶ **Ask:** How do you think a satellite might be helpful to a scientist studying penguins in Antarctica? Answers will vary. Children may say that the satellite can be used to take pictures of the penguins.

2. Teach

Share and Talk

Read pp. 160–161 together. Pair children up, then have them take turns summarizing what the satellites help the scientists learn about penguins.

Ask: This article describes a food chain. What living things are in this food chain? Which plant or animal gets eaten first? The living things in this food chain are algae, krill, and penguins. Algae are eaten first by krill. Then the penguins eat the krill.

Life Along the Ice

Read Together

Scientists working with NASA use satellites to study the ocean. The satellites are in space. Some scientists study how animals live in their environments. Many penguins live in the ocean near Antarctica.

160

Big Idea	Teacher Background
Scientists can use satellites to learn about Earth.	▶ The NASA satellites were used to study small pockets of open ocean water that, when warmed by the Sun, produce microscopic plant life. By measuring the ocean temperatures around Antarctica, the scientists were able to predict how quickly the microscopic plant life, or algae, would grow. This helped them know if the penguin population would rise or fall.

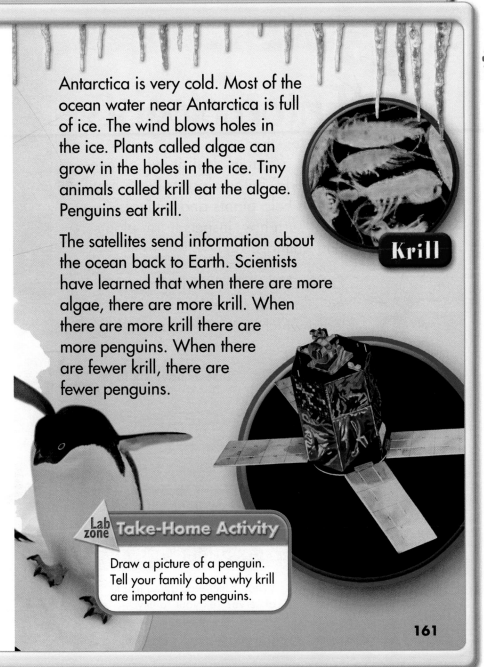

Antarctica is very cold. Most of the ocean water near Antarctica is full of ice. The wind blows holes in the ice. Plants called algae can grow in the holes in the ice. Tiny animals called krill eat the algae. Penguins eat krill.

Krill

The satellites send information about the ocean back to Earth. Scientists have learned that when there are more algae, there are more krill. When there are more krill there are more penguins. When there are fewer krill, there are fewer penguins.

Lab zone Take-Home Activity

Draw a picture of a penguin. Tell your family about why krill are important to penguins.

161

3. Summarize

QUICK Summary

▶ NASA satellites provide scientists with information about the ocean around Antarctica.

▶ Scientists use the satellite information to try to understand how much algae is growing in the icy water near Antarctica.

▶ Scientists have learned that the size of the penguin population in Antarctica changes depending on the populations of krill and algae.

Digital Classroom

www.nasa.gov To learn more about Antarctic penguins, krill, and algae, go to the NASA Web site to find information that you can share with children.

Take-Home Activity

Tips for Success

▶ Have children study a picture of a penguin before making their drawing. Ask them to make their drawings as detailed as possible.

▶ Encourage children to use scientific terms, such as *food chain*, when they tell their families about the relationship between penguins and krill.

California English-Language Arts
CONTENT STANDARDS FOCUS

1RW1.16 Word Analysis, Fluency, and Systematic Vocabulary Development Read aloud with fluency in a manner that sounds like natural speech.

Objective Students read about and discuss what entomologists do.

Career
⏱ 25 min

1. Build Background

Warm Up
Activate Prior Knowledge

▶ Have children tell what they know about insects.

▶ **Ask:** Suppose a scientist studied insects. What kinds of things about insects do you think the scientist would want to find out? Possible answer: Entomologists might study how insects survive or how they get food.

▶ Write children's responses in a chart and revisit at the end of the discussion.

2. Teach

Share and Talk

Read p. 162 together. Then discuss with children what questions they would ask if they could interview an entomologist. Help children to write questions such as:

▶ How do you study insects?

▶ What kinds of insects do you study?

▶ What are some ways that insects can be used to help humans?

Have English learners tell some questions they would like to ask an entomologist.

3. Summarize and Assess

▶ Have children create a word web that describes what entomologists do. Help children write the word *entomologists* in the center circle. Then have them reread the Career to help them complete the web.

▶ After children have created their word webs, discuss ways they think insects may help or harm plants and animals.

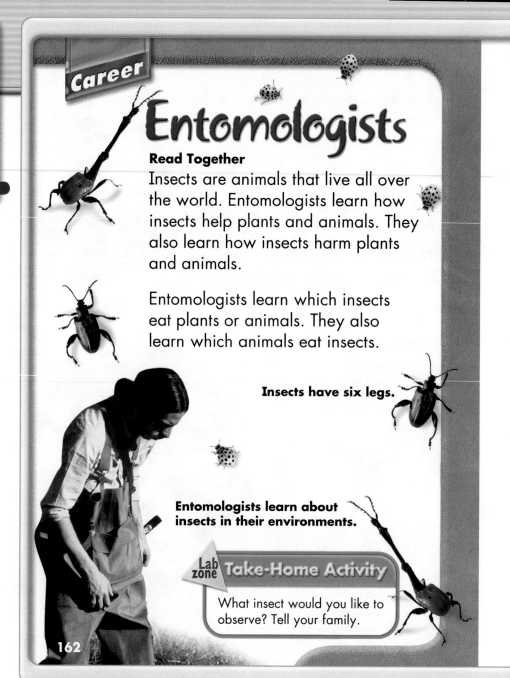

Career

Entomologists

Read Together

Insects are animals that live all over the world. Entomologists learn how insects help plants and animals. They also learn how insects harm plants and animals.

Entomologists learn which insects eat plants or animals. They also learn which animals eat insects.

Insects have six legs.

Entomologists learn about insects in their environments.

Lab zone Take-Home Activity

What insect would you like to observe? Tell your family.

162

Big Idea	Teacher Background
Entomologists learn about insects in their environments.	▶ Some insects damage crops. Some insects pass diseases on to humans. Over the years, entomologists have learned effective methods of controlling "pest" insects.
	▶ Some entomologists focus on how insects can be helpful to humans. They are called economic entomologists.

Take-Home Activity

Tips for Success

▶ Read aloud the Take-Home Activity. Then have children brainstorm a list of different insects they know about. Write these on the board.

▶ Then ask children to think about which insect they would most like to observe.

Unit B Summary

Chapter 3

What do plants and animals need?
- Plants need air, water, and energy from light to live.
- Animals need air, water, and food to live.

Chapter 4

Where do plants and animals live?
- Plants and animals live in different environments.
- Plants and animals have parts you can see that help them live in their environments.

Chapter 5

How do plants and animals live together?
- Animals eat plants or other animals for food.
- Animals may help spread seeds and may use plants or other animals for shelter.

163

1. Chapter Summaries

▸ Review the chapter summaries on p. 163 by asking children each chapter essential question and encouraging them to answer using their own words.

▸ Divide the class into groups and assign each group a major topic from the unit. Children should reread and review the text material for their assigned topic.

▸ Have each group work together to develop a visual diagram, such as a collage, diorama, or picture, for their assigned topic. Children may suggest alternate ideas for visually displaying information. Determine whether their ideas will be feasible for the class period. Encourage groups to label and use captions for all parts of their visual diagrams.

2. Reinforce Concepts

▸ Have each group present their visual diagram to the class for discussion. Encourage groups to give details that show how their topic relates to the unit's main focus. Invite children to critique the work of the other groups.

▸ After all groups have presented their visual diagrams, as a class develop a mural that forms a unified picture for the unit.

▸ When the class mural is complete, children may use it to prepare for Show What You Know (pp. 166–167) and Unit B California Standards Practice (pp. 169–172).

3. Unit Challenge

To wrap up Unit B, children should apply their knowledge about Life Sciences to answer the following questions:

What might happen to animals if plants were not in their environment?

To help children answer the question, as a class first discuss the things that plants and animals need to live. Then review the different environments that they have learned about. Finally, remind children to support their opinions by giving examples of specific plants and animals they have learned about.

Full Inquiry

20 min

1. Get Ready

Materials for Small Groups

navy bean seeds

black-eyed pea bean seeds

black bean seeds

paper plate

3 resealable plastic bags

timer (teacher use)

glue (optional)

Materials listed in *italics* are kit materials.

Preview

▶ Conduct an inventory of materials with children. For English Learners, solicit alternative names for items in their home language. Post the names of materials and other academic language, such as *experiment*.

▶ You may wish to preview science content in Chapter 4.

Advance Preparation For each group, put $\frac{1}{2}$ cup navy bean seeds (white beans) into a resealable plastic bag, 1 Tbsp black-eyed pea bean seeds (white beans with black spot) into another resealable bag, and 1 Tbsp black bean seeds into a third resealable bag.

Tips

▶ Teacher should say "Go" and "Stop" so that the hawk knows when to pick up the mice.

▶ Each hawk gets 15 seconds to pick up the mice using only one hand.

▶ Each time there is a new hawk, be sure that there are 10 black beans and 10 white beans with spots on the plate.

▶ Children may glue the beans onto their graph.

2. What to Do

Encourage Full Inquiry Preview the activity, the materials, and the steps of the scientific method with children.

Ask a question.

Read the question on p. 164 with children. Explain to children that scientific progress is made by asking meaningful questions and conducting careful investigations. Ask children to think about how they can use the materials listed to answer the question.

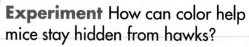

Lab zone Full Inquiry

Experiment How can color help mice stay hidden from hawks?

Use a model. White beans are the field where mice live.
 Black beans are black mice. Beans with spots are white mice.

Materials

3 bags of beans

paper plate

Ask a question.
How can color help mice stay hidden from hawks?

Make a hypothesis.
Are white beans with spots or black beans easier to see on a white background?

Plan a fair test.
Use the same number of black beans and white beans with spots.

Process Skills

You can do an **experiment** to test a **hypothesis**.

Do your test.

① One person is the hawk. The hawk must turn away.

164

Big Idea	Teacher Background
Animals have external features that help them survive in their environments.	▶ One external feature that helps an animal avoid predators is camouflage. Camouflage is a shape or color that makes an animal or plant hard to see. ▶ A few animals, such as stick insects and chameleons, are particularly well-known for their striking camouflage, but many animals have coloration that matches their habitats.

2 Put the white beans on the plate. Add 10 black beans and 10 white beans with spots. Mix the beans.

3 Listen for "Go" and "Stop." Let the hawk turn around and pick up mice with one hand.

4 Take turns being the hawk. Record how many beans you pick up.

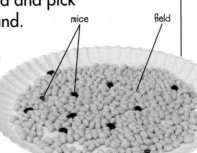

mice   field

Collect and record data.
Record what you **observe** on a bar graph.

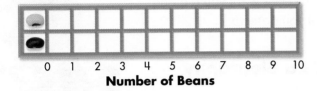

0 1 2 3 4 5 6 7 8 9 10
Number of Beans

Tell your conclusion.
Which beans were harder to see? Which mice are harder to see in a white environment?

White beans with black spots; white mice

Go Further

What might happen if you added red beans? Do an experiment to find out.

165

Digital Classroom

 Activity Video Prepare for and rehearse the activity before class.

 Printable Activity Rubric Monitor children's progress using the Activity Rubric located at **www.sfsuccessnet.com**.

 Printable LabZone Activity Provide children with additional activities located at **www.sfsuccessnet.com**.

Call **1-888-537-4908** with activity questions.

Independent Full Inquiry Modifications challenge children to test different hypotheses. Help each group write a new hypothesis that can form the basis of a follow-up experiment. For instance, what would happen if the "field" were white with spots and the "mice" were white and black? Or what if there were fewer mice of each color in the field? Encourage children to design a new experiment and find out.

Make a hypothesis.
Encourage children to phrase a hypothesis as an If . . . , then . . . statement.

Possible answers:

▶ If beans look more like the background, then they will be harder to find and pick up.

▶ If mice blend into their environment, then hawks will not be able to catch them as easily.

Plan a fair test.
Discuss with children the difference between the types of variables. Help them understand that the number of mice for the hawk to find and the amount of time the hawk has to find the mice are always the same.

Do your test.
Now children should begin the activity following the instructions provided in the Student Edition.

Teacher Talk

▶ Inform children that their school library media center may have many books with information and stories about plants and animals that live in a variety of environments.

▶ Discuss with children different environments and the different plants and animals that live in each environment.

3. Explain Your Results

Collect and record data.
After each hawk has picked up mice, have children count the number of black beans and the number of white beans with black spots that they were able to pick up. Have children create a bar graph by marking the numbers of beans on their graphs. Alternatively, have them glue the actual beans to the graph.

Tell your conclusion.
Invite children to compare their results with their hypotheses. Suggest that they write down and then explain their conclusion to the class as a group.

Science Study Notebook
 Printable Resources Activity Recording Sheet
Discuss the results of the activity by reviewing completed pp. 72–73. Ask volunteers to summarize the activity and explain the meaning of the graph. What difference did the color of the beans make?

Activity Rubric Use *Science Study Notebook Teacher's Guide* p. T30 to evaluate children's work.

Go Further

▶ Guide children to consider other ways that mice might blend into their environments, and have them suggest ways of exploring their ideas. What might happen if you added red beans?

▶ Encourage children to investigate a question like this on their own.

Life Sciences Plants and animals meet their needs in different ways.

Objective Students perform activities to demonstrate mastery of science content standards from Unit B.

Show What You Know ⏱ 30 min

Culminating Activities

Make a Model Remind children that their models should be accurate. For example, if they show a desert environment, it should include only desert plants and animals. Use the activity rubric below to score children's models.

4	The child creates an extremely detailed model that accurately depicts a specific environment. The model correctly shows what plants and animals need to live.
3	The child creates a model of a specific environment. The model correctly shows some things that plants and animals need to live.
2	The child creates a model that does not focus on a specific environment. The model shows some things that plants and animals need to live.
1	The child creates a model that does not focus on a specific environment. The model does not show what plants and animals need to live.

Show What You Know

Make a Model

- Use a shoebox to make a model environment.
- Show plants and animals.
- Show things plants and animals need to live.

Observe Your Teeth

- Try this activity at home. Look at your teeth in a mirror.
- Draw the shapes of different teeth you have. Eat an apple. Observe how you use different teeth as you eat.
- Tell the class what you did and what you observed.

Write a Biography

Talk to an adult who likes to grow plants. Ask that person how he or she grows plants. Write a story about that person and growing plants.

166

Read More About Life Sciences!

Look for other books about Life Sciences in your library media center. One book you may want to read is:

Biggest, Strongest, Fastest
by Steve Jenkins

This book shows and tells about animals that are the biggest and smallest, fastest and slowest, or strongest and longest.

167

Read More About Life Sciences

1LS2.a **Life Sciences** Students know different plants and animals inhabit different kinds of environments and have external features that help them thrive in different kinds of places.

Biggest, Strongest, Fastest by Steve Jenkins
ISBN 0-6881-5283-X

Related Titles

Across the Big Blue Sea: An Ocean Wildlife Book by Jakki Wood
ISBN 0-7922-7308-7

Who Eats What? Food Chains and Food Webs by Patricia Lauber
ISBN 0-0644-5130-5

Who Lives in the Snow? by Jennifer Berry Jones
ISBN 1-5709-8287-2

Observe Your Teeth Before children do the activity, invite them to look at a partner's teeth in order to tell which teeth are sharp or flat. Encourage children to make their drawings as accurate as possible. Use the activity rubric below to score children's drawings. Keep in mind that some children may be missing teeth.

4	Drawing accurately depicts both sharp and flat teeth. Many teeth are drawn clearly and correctly.
3	Drawing shows sharp and flat teeth. Some of the teeth are drawn clearly and correctly.
2	Drawing shows sharp and flat teeth. Few teeth are drawn.
1	Drawing shows no distinction between sharp and flat teeth or does not resemble the teeth of a person.

Write a Biography Remind children to focus their story on how the person grows plants. Encourage them to include details about how plants grow. Use the writing rubric below to score children's stories.

4	Story identifies a real-life person who enjoys growing plants. It provides a detailed description of how the person grows plants and includes many facts. All of the information about plant growth is accurate.
3	Story describes a real-life person who enjoys growing plants, and tells how the person grows them. Story includes several facts about plant growth.
2	Story discusses how to grow plants, but there is no real-life person described. Some of the details about plant growth are inaccurate.
1	Story wanders off-subject. It includes a person as one of its characters but does not go into any detail about growing plants.

1IE4.0 Investigation and Experimentation
Scientific progress is made by asking meaningful questions and conducting careful investigations. As a basis for understanding this concept and addressing the content in the other three strands, students should develop their own questions and perform investigations.

Objective Children design and conduct scientific experiments, then use the evidence they obtain to draw conclusions and make inferences.

Science Fair Projects
⏱ 30 min

1. Introduce

Remind children that scientists try to explain puzzling events and test their hypotheses through experiments. Inform children that they have the opportunity to ask meaningful questions and conduct careful experiments in an independent project.

2. Plan and Experiment

As children develop their projects, encourage them to:

▶ identify variables (things that can change).

▶ tell what they will change on purpose and what they will measure throughout the experiment.

▶ decide if their results address their original question.

3. Communicate

Explain to children that an experiment is not complete until findings are presented in written or oral form. Remind children that to be valid, science experiments need a larger sample test group than just one plant. Encourage students to use at least three plants for each experiment. Each child must draw a conclusion or make an inference based on evidence from the experiment.

Encourage children to use charts, graphs, or other tools for more effective communication. If necessary, work with children to demonstrate how to interpret the data they display. Children may communicate their results in a variety of ways, such as written or oral reports, class discussions, or poster presentations.

Safety Notes

▶ Approach laboratory experiences in a serious and courteous manner.

▶ Clean up any spill immediately.

▶ Keep work area clean.

▶ Clean the laboratory area before leaving.

▶ Wash hands with soap and water after completing an experiment.

Discovery CHANNEL SCHOOL Science Fair Projects

Full Inquiry

Using Scientific Methods
1. Ask a question.
2. Make a hypothesis.
3. Plan a fair test.
4. Do your test.
5. Record what happens.
6. Tell your conclusions.
7. Go further.

Idea 1
Growing Plants in Soil and Sand

Plan a project.

Find out if plants grow better in soil or sand.

Idea 2
Fresh Water and Salt Water

Plan a project. Find out if plants grow better with fresh water or salt water.

168

Big Idea

Scientific progress is made by asking meaningful questions and conducting careful investigations.

Teacher Background

▶ You can help children learn how to think of good questions and how to evaluate their questions independently by providing them with this framework:

• First, think about what you know. Ask a question about what you want to learn.

• Next, ask yourself if the question can be answered by doing an investigation in the classroom.

• Then, ask yourself if you can answer your question with the equipment and materials that are available in the classroom.

• Finally, ask yourself if you can answer the question in a reasonable amount of time.

Unit B California Standards Practice

Write the letter of the correct answer.

1. What do plants need to live?

   A water, air, and light

   B light only

   C water only

   D animals only

2. What do animals need to live?

   A food only

   B water only

   C light only

   D water, air, and food

169

The California Science Standards Test is administered as part of the California Standardized Testing and Reporting (STAR) Program. The questions on these pages provide an opportunity for children to practice the language and format of the science standards test.

Released test items are available online through the California Department of Education Web site at **www.cde.ca.gov/ta/tg/sr/resources.asp**.

1 The correct answer is **A** (water, air, and light). **1LS2.b**
Answer Strategy: Plants need water, air, and light to live, so B and C are incorrect. Some plants may depend upon animals for some things, but they need more than only animals to live, so D is incorrect.

2 The correct answer is **D** (water, air, and food). **1LS2.b**
Answer Strategy: Animals need water, air, and food to live, so A, B, and C are incorrect.

Intervention and Reteaching

California Science CONTENT STANDARDS FOCUS	Item Number	Student Edition	Content Readers	Science Study Notebook	Intervention Study Guide
1LS2.b Students know both plants and animals need water, animals need food, and plants need light.	1	80–81	• **Below-Level** *Needs of Plants and Animals* • **On-Level** *Plants and Animals*	38	22–23
1LS2.b Students know both plants and animals need water, animals need food, and plants need light.	2	86–87	• **Below-Level** *Needs of Plants and Animals* • **On-Level** *Plants and Animals*	40	26–27

Resources

3 The correct answer is **C** (thick fat called blubber).
1LS2.a

Answer Strategy: B and D are incorrect because whales do not have fur or gills. Whales do have fins, but fins do not keep whales warm, so A is incorrect.

4 The correct answer is **D** (The leaves help the plant keep water.). **1LS2.a**

Answer Strategy: Waxy leaves do not protect plants from animals or from other plants, so A and B are incorrect. C is incorrect because there is little water in a desert, and leaves would need to keep water, not let it out. So, D is correct.

Unit B California Standards Practice

3. **What do whales have to keep them warm in the water?**

   A fins
   B fur
   C thick fat called blubber
   D gills

4. **How do small waxy leaves help a plant live in the desert?**

   A The leaves protect it from other plants.
   B The leaves protect it from animals.
   C The leaves let water out.
   D The leaves help the plant keep water.

170

Intervention and Reteaching

Resources

California Science CONTENT STANDARDS FOCUS	Item Number	Student Edition	Content Readers	Science Study Notebook	Intervention Study Guide
1LS2.a Students know different plants and animals inhabit different kinds of environments and have external features that help them thrive in different kinds of places.	3	112–113	• **Below-Level** *Environments* • **On-Level** *Different Environments*	52	32–33
1LS2.a Students know different plants and animals inhabit different kinds of environments and have external features that help them thrive in different kinds of places.	4	114–115	• **Below-Level** *Environments* • **On-Level** *Different Environments*	53	34–35

Unit B California Standards Practice

5. How do giraffes use their long necks?

  A to walk slowly
  B to run fast
  C to reach leaves at the top of trees
  D to get air from water

6. What do some animals use for shelter and nesting?

  A air
  B food
  C water
  D plants or other animals

---

5 The correct answer is **C** (to reach leaves at the top of trees). **1LS2.a**

Answer Strategy: A and B do not make sense; giraffes do not need long necks to walk or run. D is not correct because giraffes do not get air from water.

6 The correct answer is **D** (plants or other animals). **1LS2.c**

Answer Strategy: Children should recognize that air, food, and water are basic needs of animals, not materials for shelter or nesting. So A, B, and C do not answer the question.

Intervention and Reteaching

Resources

California Science CONTENT STANDARDS FOCUS	Item Number	Student Edition	Content Readers	Science Study Notebook	Intervention Study Guide
1LS2.a Students know different plants and animals inhabit different kinds of environments and have external features that help them thrive in different kinds of places.	5	104–105	• **Below-Level** *Environments* • **On-Level** *Different Environments*	50	28–29
1LS2.c Students know animals eat plants or other animals for food and may also use plants or even other animals for shelter and nesting.	6	134–135	• **Below-Level** *Plants and Animals Living Together* • **On-Level** *Animals and Plants Live Together*	64	36–37

7 The correct answer is **B** (plant, insect, bird). **1LS2.c**

Answer Strategy: Choices A and D include a part of a plant in addition to the plant itself, so they do not make sense. Similarly, choice C contains two parts of a plant, so B is correct.

8 The correct answer is **A** (other animals). **1LS2.d**

Answer Strategy: The drawing shows an animal with sharp, pointy teeth. Many animals with sharp, pointy teeth eat other animals. The other choices are plants or parts of plants, and animals that eat plants usually have some flat teeth.

7. **Which list tells a food chain?**

   A plant, leaf, frog
   B plant, insect, bird
   C insect, root, leaf
   D insect, plant, root

8. **Look at the teeth of the animal in the picture. What does this animals eat?**

   A other animals
   B vegetables
   C flowers
   D plants

172

Intervention and Reteaching

Resources

California Science CONTENT STANDARDS FOCUS	Item Number	Student Edition	Content Readers	Science Study Notebook	Intervention Study Guide
1LS2.c Students know animals eat plants or other animals for food and may also use plants or even other animals for shelter and nesting.	7	138–139	• **Below- Level** *Plants and Animals Living Together* • **On-Level** *Animals and Plants Live Together*	66	40–41
1LS2.d Students know how to infer what animals eat from the shapes of their teeth (e.g., sharp teeth: eats meat; flat teeth: eats plants).	8	148–151	• **Below-Level** *Plants and Animals Living Together* • **On-Level** *Animals and Plants Live Together*	69	46–47

NOTES

NOTES

NOTES

NOTES

NOTES

RESOURCES FOR TEACHERS AND STUDENTS

ISBN 0-328-24124-5

School-to-Home Communication

To the Teacher

As stated in the Science Framework for California Public Schools, "California is a world leader in science and technology and, as a result, enjoys both prosperity and a wealth of intellectual talent. The nation and the state of California have a history that is rich in innovation and invention. Educators have the opportunity to foster and inspire in students an interest in science. . . ."

Inspiring in students an interest in science is an important goal for Pearson Education and *Scott Foresman California Science*. As an elementary educator, you are developing foundational skills for life-long learning. Partnering with you on this quest are parents, guardians, and other caregivers involved in their children's education. By helping them understand what their children are learning in school, you are developing an educational partnership that enriches the educational experience for all participants. *Scott Foresman California Science* is designed to assist you in promoting school-to-home communication.

The **School-to-Home Letter** is a communication tool created to engage parents, guardians, and other caregivers in their children's science learning experiences. The letters are provided in English and Spanish.

School-to-Home Letters are designed to

- follow each chapter.

- summarize the main ideas of the chapter.

- provide educational family activities.

- review science vocabulary terms.

The **Student Progress Report** is a recording tool created to track student mastery of the Science Content Standards for California Public Schools. The Student Progress Report is also a communication tool to inform parents, guardians, and other caregivers of their children's understanding of science concepts.

Student Progress Reports are designed to

- follow each unit.

- connect the learning experiences outlined in the School-to-Home Letters with mastery of the Science Content Standards.

- track which students need more help and where classroom science instruction needs to be reinforced, reviewed, or expanded.

- provide interim, informal progress reports to send home.

At Pearson Education, we believe that family involvement in their children's education enhances the learning experience and contributes to the motivation and encouragement that you provide every day.

ISBN 0-328-22261-5

School to Home Letter

Scott Foresman California Science

Chapter 1: Observing Solids, Liquids, and Gases

California Standard
Physical Sciences 1.0 Materials come in different forms (states), including solids, liquids, and gases.

Here are the key concepts we are learning:

- A property is something you can observe with your senses.
- Shape, size, color, and how something feels are properties.
- A solid has its own shape and size.
- A liquid takes the shape of its container.
- A liquid has its own amount or size.
- Air is a gas.
- A gas can change shape and size.
- Solids, liquids, and gases are different from each other.
- Shape or size are ways solids, liquids, and gases can be different.

Vocabulary Review

Your child will learn these vocabulary words:

✓ **property**
✓ **solid**
✓ **liquid**
✓ **gas**

Review these words with your child. Ask him or her to identify a book, water, and air as a solid, liquid, or gas. Have your child write sentences that tell the properties of each example.

Take-Home Activities

Math in Science One object can be used to describe the position of another object. Together, gather several blocks of different colors, shapes, and sizes. Ask your child to tell you where to put each block as you build a tower or another shape.

NASA Objects weigh more on Earth than on the Moon. Have your child draw a picture of himself or herself on the Moon and share it with the family. Then ask why he or she would weigh less on the Moon.

NASA Career Material scientists at NASA work to make things that are durable in space. Help your child find a tissue, a paper towel, and a piece of cloth. Have him or her test if each object can hold a spoon when it is wet. Ask your child to share with the family what he or she learned.

Carta De la escuela al hogar

Ciencias Scott Foresman para California

Capítulo 1: Observar sólidos, líquidos y gases

Estándar de California

Ciencias físicas 1.0   Los materiales existen en diferentes formas (estados), que incluyen sólidos, líquidos y gases.

Éstos son los conceptos clave que estamos aprendiendo:

- Una propiedad es algo que se puede percibir con los sentidos.

- La forma, el tamaño, el color y la textura son propiedades.

- Un sólido tiene una forma y tamaño propios.

- Un líquido toma la forma del recipiente que lo contiene.

- Un líquido tiene su propia cantidad o tamaño.

- El aire es un gas.

- Un gas puede cambiar de forma y tamaño.

- Los sólidos, los líquidos y los gases son diferentes unos de otros.

- La forma o el tamaño son aspectos en que los sólidos, los líquidos y los gases son diferentes.

Repaso del vocabulario

Su niño o niña aprenderá estas palabras de vocabulario:

- ✓ **propiedad**
- ✓ **sólido**
- ✓ **líquido**
- ✓ **gas**

Repase estas palabras con su niño o niña. Pídale que identifique un libro, agua y aire como sólido, líquido o gas. Pídale a su niño o niña que escriba oraciones que indiquen las propiedades de cada ejemplo.

Actividades para el hogar

Matemáticas en las ciencias Se puede usar un objeto para describir la posición de otro objeto. Junten bloques de diferentes colores, formas y tamaños. Pídale a su niño o niña que le diga dónde debe poner cada bloque mientras construye una torre u otra figura.

NASA Los objetos pesan más en la Tierra que en la Luna. Pídale a su niño o niña que dibuje una foto de él o ella en la Luna y se la muestre a la familia. Después, pregúntele por qué él o ella pesaría menos en la Luna.

NASA Profesión Los científicos de la NASA especializados en materiales trabajan para hacer cosas que sean durables en el espacio. Ayude a su niño o niña a buscar un pañuelo desechable, una toalla de papel y un trozo de tela. Pídale que pruebe si cada material puede sostener una cuchara cuando está mojado. Pídale a su niño o niña que le muestre a la familia lo que aprendió.

School to Home Letter

Chapter 2: Changing Solids, Liquids, and Gases

Scott Foresman California Science

California Standard
Physical Sciences 1.0   Materials come in different forms (states), including solids, liquids, and gases.

Here are the key concepts we are learning:

- Things can change when they are mixed, cooled, or heated.
- Color, size, shape, and how something feels are properties that can change.
- Solids can be mixed with liquids.
- Some solids dissolve when they are mixed with liquids.
- Cooling can freeze water into solid ice.
- Heating can change ice back into water.
- Heating can cause water to evaporate.
- A cooked egg cannot change back to the way it was.

Vocabulary Review

Your child will learn these vocabulary words:

- ✓ **melt**
- ✓ **dissolve**
- ✓ **freeze**
- ✓ **evaporate**

Review these words with your child. Ask him or her to write sentences telling what happens when water freezes, melts, and evaporates.

Take-Home Activities

Math in Science Your child will learn that objects come in different forms. Together, find examples of different solids, liquids, and gases in a room in your home. Help your child make a bar graph that shows how many of each example you found.

Biography Annette Baron is a glassblower who turns melted glass into art. Help your child learn about how glass is blown by experimenting with a balloon together. Have him or her insert a straw into a balloon and blow into the straw. Ask your child to write about what happens to the balloon.

Carta De la escuela al hogar

Ciencias Scott Foresman para California

Capítulo 2: Los cambios de los sólidos, los líquidos y los gases.

Estándar de California
Ciencias físicas 1.0   Los materiales existen en diferentes formas (estados), que incluyen sólidos, líquidos y gases.

Éstos son los conceptos clave que estamos aprendiendo:

- Las cosas pueden cambiar al mezclarlas, enfriarlas o calentarlas.

- El color, el tamaño, la forma y la textura son propiedades que pueden cambiar.

- Los sólidos pueden ser mezclarse con líquidos.

- Algunos sólidos se disuelven al mezclarlos con líquidos.

- Al enfriar el agua, ésta puede transformarse en hielo sólido.

- Al calentarse, el hielo puede volver a convertirse en agua.

- Al calentarse, el agua se puede evaporar.

- Un huevo cocido no puede volver a su forma anterior.

Repaso del vocabulario

Su niño o niña aprenderá estas palabras de vocabulario:

- ✓ **derretirse**
- ✓ **disolverse**
- ✓ **congelarse**
- ✓ **evaporarse**

Repase estas palabras con su niño o niña. Pídale que escriba oraciones que indiquen lo que pasa cuando el agua se congela, se derrite y se evapora.

Actividades para el hogar

Matemáticas en las ciencias Su niño o niña aprenderá que los objetos tienen diferentes formas. Juntos, busquen ejemplos de diferentes sólidos, líquidos y gases en una habitación de su hogar. Ayude a su niño o niña a hacer una gráfica de barras que muestre los ejemplos que encontraron.

Biografía Annette Baron es una sopladora de vidrio que transforma el vidrio derretido en arte. Experimente con su niño o niña usando un globo para ayudarle a aprender cómo se sopla el vidrio. Pídale que coloque una pajilla dentro del globo y que luego sople. Pídale que escriba lo que sucede con el globo.

School to Home Letter

Chapter 3: Needs of Plants and Animals

California Standard
Life Sciences 2.0   Plants and animals meet their needs in different ways.

Here are the key concepts we are learning:

- Plants need air, water, and light to live.

- Plants get light from the Sun.

- Roots take in water and nutrients from the soil.

- Green leaves take in energy from sunlight and make food for the plant.

- Animals need water and air to live.

- Animals need food too.

Vocabulary Review

Your child will learn these vocabulary words:

- ✓ **living**
- ✓ **roots**
- ✓ **nutrients**
- ✓ **leaves**

Review these words with your child. Ask your child to draw pictures that show or relate to them. Then have your child write a sentence for each word.

Take-Home Activities

Math in Science Tally marks help us record information. Help your child make a tally chart. Have him or her record the number of plants and animals you can find together around your home.

Career Your child will learn that some naturalists are working to save the California condor. Ask your child to share with the family what he or she learned about the naturalists' efforts. Have your child talk about how naturalists have added to the number of California condors living in the wild.

Carta De la escuela al hogar

Ciencias Scott Foresman para California

Capítulo 3: Las necesidades de las plantas y de los animales

Estándar de California

Ciencias de la vida 2.0   Las plantas y los animales satisfacen sus necesidades de diferentes maneras.

Éstos son los conceptos clave que estamos aprendiendo:

- Las plantas necesitan aire, agua y luz para vivir.
- Las plantas obtienen luz del Sol.
- Las raíces absorben el agua y los nutrientes del suelo.
- Las hojas verdes reciben la energia del Sol y producen alimento para la planta.
- Los animales necesitan agua y aire para vivir.
- Los animales también necesitan alimento.

Repaso del vocabulario

Su niño o niña aprenderá estas palabras de vocabulario:

- ✓ **vivos**
- ✓ **raíces**
- ✓ **nutrientes**
- ✓ **hojas**

Repase estas palabras con su niño o niña. Pídale que haga dibujos que muestren o estén relacionados con cada palabra. Después, pídale a su niño o niña que escriba una oración con cada palabra.

Actividades para el hogar

Matemáticas en las ciencias Las marcas de conteo nos ayudan a registrar información. Ayude a su niño o niña a hacer una tabla de conteo. Pídale que anote el número de plantas y animales que encuentren juntos alrededor de su hogar.

Profesión Su niño o niña aprenderá que algunos naturalistas están trabajando para salvar el cóndor de California. Pídale a su niño o niña que comparta con la familia lo que aprendió acerca de los esfuerzos de los naturalistas. Pídale que comente lo que han hecho los naturalistas para aumentar el número de cóndores de California que viven en libertad.

School to Home Letter

Chapter 4: Environments

California Standard
Life Sciences 2.0 Plants and animals meet their needs in different ways.

Here are the key concepts we are learning:

- An environment is a place where plants and animals live.
- Plants and animals have parts that help them live in their environment.
- A forest is an environment.
- Many different plants and animals have parts that help them to live in a forest.
- An ocean is an environment.
- Many different plants and animals have parts that help them to live in an ocean.
- A desert is an environment.
- Many different plants and animals have parts that help them to live in a desert.

Vocabulary Review

Your child will learn these vocabulary words:

- ✓ **environment**
- ✓ **forest**
- ✓ **ocean**
- ✓ **desert**

Help your child find pictures in magazines that show or relate to each word. Paste the pictures onto cards and label them. Then have your child write a sentence for each word.

Take-Home Activities

Math in Science A bar graph is one way to record information. Help your child choose an environment. Have him or her draw plants and animals that live in the environment. Together, make a bar graph and show to the family how many plants and animals are in your child's picture.

Biography Dr. Sonia Ortega is a marine biologist who does careful studies of ocean animals. Help your child find a place near your home where plants and animals live. Ask him or her to study the place and draw a picture of what he or she observes.

Carta De la escuela al hogar

Capítulo 4: Ambientes

Estándar de California
Ciencias de la vida 2.0   Las plantas y los animales satisfacen sus necesidades de diferentes maneras.

Éstos son los conceptos clave que estamos aprendiendo:

- Un ambiente es un lugar donde viven plantas y animales.

- Las plantas y los animales tienen partes que les permiten vivir en sus ambientes.

- Un bosque es un ambiente.

- Muchas plantas y animales diferentes tienen partes que les permiten vivir en un bosque.

- Un océano es un ambiente.

- Muchas plantas y animales diferentes tienen partes que les permiten vivir en un océano.

- Un desierto es un ambiente.

- Muchas plantas y animales diferentes tienen partes que les permiten vivir en un desierto.

Repaso del vocabulario

Su niño o niña aprenderá estas palabras de vocabulario:

- ✓ **ambiente**
- ✓ **bosque**
- ✓ **océano**
- ✓ **desierto**

Ayude a su niño o niña a buscar en revistas fotos que muestren o se relacionen con cada palabra. Peguen las fotos en tarjetas y rotúlenlas. Después, pídale a su niño o niña que escriba una oración con cada palabra.

Actividades para el hogar

Matemáticas en las ciencias Una gráfica de barras es una manera de registrar información. Ayude a su niño o niña a elegir un ambiente. Pídale que dibuje plantas y animales que viven en ese ambiente. Hagan juntos una gráfica de barras para mostrarle a la familia cuántas plantas y animales hay en la ilustración de su niño o niña.

Biografía La doctora Sonia Ortega es una bióloga marina que hace estudios detallados de animales del océano. Ayude a su niño o niña a buscar un lugar cerca de su hogar en donde vivan plantas y animales. Pídale que estudie el lugar y que haga un dibujo de lo que observe.

School to Home Letter

Scott Foresman California Science

Chapter 5: Plants and Animals Living Together

California Standard
Life Sciences 2.0   Plants and animals meet their needs in different ways.

Here are the key concepts we are learning:

- Animals need plants or other animals for food and shelter or nesting.

- Some animals carry seeds to new places where they can grow.

- Some animals bury seeds and they grow.

- Plants use energy from sunlight to make food, and plants are eaten by animals that are then eaten by other animals.

- Desert plants and animals depend on each other through food chains.

- Marsh plants and animals depend on each other through food chains.

- Animals with sharp, pointed teeth eat other animals for food. Animals with flat teeth eat plants for food.

Vocabulary Review

Your child will learn these vocabulary words:

- ✓ **shelter**
- ✓ **food chain**
- ✓ **marsh**

Review these words with your child. Have him or her draw pictures of each and then write a sentence for each word.

Take-Home Activities

Math in Science Venn diagrams help us determine what is different and similar about various things. Help your child find and sort through pictures of animals. Then have your child make a Venn diagram that shows what the animals eat.

NASA Your child will learn that scientists at NASA use satellites to study life in Antarctica.

Have your child draw a picture of a penguin. Ask him or her to explain to the family why krill are important to penguins.

Career Entomologists study insects in their environments. Ask your child to choose an insect that he or she would like to observe. Then have your child share with the family what he or she learned.

Carta De la escuela al hogar

Ciencias Scott Foresman para California

Capítulo 5: Las plantas y los animales viven juntos

Estándar de California
Ciencias de la vida 2.0   Las plantas y los animales satisfacen sus necesidades de diferentes maneras.

Éstos son los conceptos clave que estamos aprendiendo:

- Los animales necesitan de las plantas o de otros animales para alimentarse, refugiarse o anidar.

- Algunos animales llevan semillas a lugares nuevos, donde éstas pueden crecer.

- Algunos animales entierran semillas y éstas crecen.

- Las plantas usan la energía del Sol para transformarla en alimento. Las plantas sirven de alimento para los animales que son, a su vez, el alimento de otros animales.

- Las plantas y los animales del desierto dependen unos de otros en cadenas alimentarias.

- Las plantas y los animales de una marisma dependen unos de otros en cadenas alimentarias.

- Los animales con dientes afilados y puntiagudos se alimentan de otros animales. Los animales con los dientes planos se alimentan de plantas.

Repaso del vocabulario

Su niño o niña aprenderá estas palabras de vocabulario:

- ✓ refugio
- ✓ cadena alimentaria
- ✓ marisma

Repase estas palabras con su niño o niña. Pídale que haga un dibujo y que escriba una oración con cada palabra.

Actividades para el hogar

Matemáticas en las ciencias Los diagramas de Venn nos ayudan a determinar las semejanzas y las diferencias entre varias cosas. Ayude a su niño o niña a buscar y clasificar fotos de animales. Después, pídale que haga un diagrama de Venn que muestre lo que comen los animales.

NASA Su niño o niña aprenderá que los científicos de la NASA usan satélites para estudiar la vida en la Antártida. Pídale a su niño o niña que dibuje un pingüino. Pídale que le explique a la familia por qué el camarón antártico es importante para los pingüinos.

Profesión Los entomólogos estudian los insectos en sus ambientes. Pídale a su niño o niña que elija un insecto que le gustaría observar. Después, pídale que le muestre a la familia lo que aprendió.

School to Home Letter

Scott Foresman California Science

Chapter 6: Observing Weather

California Standard
Earth Sciences 3.0 Weather can be observed, measured, and described.

Here are the key concepts we are learning:

- Weather is what it is like outside.
- A wind vane tells which way the wind is blowing.
- Temperature is how hot or cold something is.
- A thermometer is a tool that measures temperature.
- A rain gauge is a tool to measure rain.
- The numbers show how much rain falls.
- Light from the Sun warms land, water, and air.

Vocabulary Review

Your child will learn these vocabulary words:

- ✓ **weather**
- ✓ **wind vane**
- ✓ **temperature**
- ✓ **thermometer**
- ✓ **rain gauge**

Review these words with your child. Have him or her draw pictures of each and then write a sentence for each word.

Take-Home Activities

Math in Science San Francisco gets about 52 centimeters of rain each year. Look at the bar graph on page 191 of the textbook together with your child. Ask your child if San Francisco usually gets more rain in spring or fall. Have your child share with the family what he or she learned.

NASA NASA sends satellites with different functions into space. Have your child draw a picture of a satellite and share it with the family. Then ask him or her to tell the family how satellites can help scientists learn about weather on Earth.

NASA Career A meteorologist is a scientist who studies or predicts the weather. Together with your child, look at a weather map in a newspaper. Ask him or her what the weather might be like tomorrow.

Carta De la escuela al hogar

Ciencias Scott Foresman para California

Capítulo 6: Observar el estado del tiempo

Estándar de California
Ciencias de la Tierra 3.0   El clima se puede observar, medir y describir.

Éstos son los conceptos clave que estamos aprendiendo:

- El estado del tiempo son las condiciones al aire libre.

- Una veleta nos muestra la dirección en que sopla el viento.

- La temperatura indica qué tan caliente o qué tan frío está algo.

- Un termómetro es un instrumento que mide la temperatura.

- Un pluviómetro es un instrumento que se usa para medir cuánta lluvia ha caído.

- Los números muestran cuánta lluvia ha caído.

- La luz del Sol calienta el suelo, el agua y el aire.

Repaso del vocabulario

Su niño o niña aprenderá estas palabras de vocabulario:

- ✓ **estado del tiempo**
- ✓ **veleta**
- ✓ **temperatura**
- ✓ **termómetro**
- ✓ **pluviómetro**

Repase estas palabras con su niño o niña. Pídale que haga un dibujo de cada una y que escriba una oración con cada palabra.

Actividades para el hogar

Matemáticas en las ciencias En San Francisco caen aproximadamente 52 centímetros de lluvia cada año. Mire con su niño o niña la gráfica de barras en la página 190 del libro de texto. Pregúntele si en San Francisco cae más lluvia en primavera o en otoño. Pídale a su niño o niña que le muestre a su familia lo que aprendió.

NASA La NASA envía satélites al espacio con diferentes funciones. Pídale a su niño o niña que haga un dibujo de un satélite y que se lo muestre a su familia.

NASA Profesión Un meteorólogo es un científico que estudia o predice el tiempo. Mire con su niño o niña el mapa del estado del tiempo en un periódico. Pídale que le diga cómo va a estar el tiempo mañana.

School to Home Letter

Scott Foresman California Science

Chapter 7: Seasons

California Standard
Earth Sciences 3.0   Weather can be observed, measured, and described.

Here are the key concepts we are learning:

- A season is a time of year.
- You can predict what weather will be like in a season.
- Summer is the warmest season.
- Summer may be very dry.
- Fall is cooler than summer.
- Some fall days are rainy.
- Winter is the coldest season.
- Winter may be the wettest season too.

Vocabulary Review

Your child will learn these vocabulary words:

✓ **season**
✓ **spring**
✓ **summer**
✓ **fall**
✓ **winter**

Review these words with your child. Have him or her pretend to be a weather reporter and report what the weather is like in each season.

Take-Home Activities

Math in Science Have your child ask friends or family members what their favorite season is. Have him or her make a chart like the one on page 217 of the textbook. Ask your child which season is the favorite of the largest number of people.

Career Your child will learn about farmers. Ask him or her to draw a picture of a farm on a warm sunny day. Have your child tell your family about farmers.

Carta De la escuela al hogar

Ciencias Scott Foresman para California

Capítulo 7: Las estaciones

Estándar de California
Ciencias de la Tierra 3.0   El estado del tiempo se puede observar, medir y describir.

Éstos son los conceptos clave que estamos aprendiendo:

- Una estación es una época del año.

- Puedes predecir el estado del tiempo de una estación.

- El verano es la estación más cálida.

- El verano puede ser muy seco.

- El otoño es más fresco que el verano.

- Algunos días del otoño son lluviosos.

- El invierno es la estación más fría.

- El invierno también puede ser la estación más húmeda.

Repaso del vocabulario

Su niño o niña aprenderá estas palabras de vocabulario:

- ✓ **estación**
- ✓ **primavera**
- ✓ **verano**
- ✓ **otoño**
- ✓ **invierno**

Repase estas palabras con su niño o niña. Pídale que imagine que es un reportero del tiempo y que dé un informe del estado del tiempo en cada estación.

Actividades para el hogar

Matemáticas en las ciencias Pídale a su niño o niña que les pregunte a sus amigos, o a miembros de la familia, cuál es su estación favorita. Pídale que haga una tabla como la de la página 217 del libro de texto. Pregúntele a su niño o niña cuál es la estación favorita de la mayoría de personas.

Profesión Su niño o niña aprenderá sobre los granjeros. Pídale que haga un dibujo de una granja en un día caluroso y soleado. Pídale a su niño o niña que hable con la familia acerca de los granjeros.

GRADE 1 STUDENT PROGRESS REPORT

Copy for each student.   Scott Foresman California Science

Student Name: _____

Chapter 1	Lesson	Comments
1PS1.0 Materials come in different forms (states), including solids, liquids, and gases.	❑ Lesson 1 **1PS1.a** ❑ Lesson 2 **1PS1.a** ❑ Lesson 3 **1PS1.a** ❑ Lesson 4 **1PS1.a** ❑ Lesson 5 **1PS1.a**	
1IE4.0 Scientific progress is made by asking meaningful questions and conducting careful investigations. As a basis for understanding this concept and addressing the content in the other three strands, students should develop their own questions and perform investigations. **Date:** __/__/__	❑ Directed Inquiry **1PS1.a, 1IE4.b** ❑ Guided Inquiry **1PS1.a, 1IE4.b**	
Chapter 2	**Lesson**	**Comments**
1PS1.0 Materials come in different forms (states), including solids, liquids, and gases.	❑ Lesson 1 **1PS1.b** ❑ Lesson 2 **1PS1.b** ❑ Lesson 3 **1PS1.b** ❑ Lesson 4 **1PS1.b** ❑ Lesson 5 **1PS1.b**	
1IE4.0 Scientific progress is made by asking meaningful questions and conducting careful investigations. As a basis for understanding this concept and addressing the content in the other three strands, students should develop their own questions and perform investigations. **Date:** __/__/__	❑ Directed Inquiry **1PS1.b, 1IE4.b** ❑ Guided Inquiry **1PS1.b, 1IE4.b** ❑ Full Inquiry **1PS1.b, 1IE4.a, 1IE4.b**	
Chapter 3	**Lesson**	**Comments**
1LS2.0 Plants and animals meet their needs in different ways.	❑ Lesson 1 **1 LS 2.b** ❑ Lesson 2 **1 LS 2.e** ❑ Lesson 3 **1 LS 2.b**	
1IE4.0 Scientific progress is made by asking meaningful questions and conducting careful investigations. As a basis for understanding this concept and addressing the content in the other three strands, students should develop their own questions and perform investigations. **Date:** __/__/__	❑ Directed Inquiry **1LS2.b, 1IE4.b** ❑ Guided Inquiry **1LS2.b, 1LS2.e, 1IE4.b**	
Chapter 4	**Lesson**	**Comments**
1LS2.0 Plants and animals meet their needs in different ways.	❑ Lesson 1 **1LS2.a** ❑ Lesson 2 **1LS2.a** ❑ Lesson 3 **1LS2.a** ❑ Lesson 4 **1LS2.a**	
1IE4.0 Scientific progress is made by asking meaningful questions and conducting careful investigations. As a basis for understanding this concept and addressing the content in the other three strands, students should develop their own questions and perform investigations. **Date:** __/__/__	❑ Directed Inquiry **1LS2.a, 1IE4.a** ❑ Guided Inquiry **1LS 2.a, 1IE4.a, 1IE4.b**	

Date: __/__/__

GRADE 1 STUDENT PROGRESS REPORT

Copy for each student. Scott Foresman California Science

Student Name: _____

Chapter 5	Lesson	Comments
1LS2.0 Plants and animals meet their needs in different ways.	❑ Lesson 1 **1LS2.c** ❑ Lesson 2 **1LS2.c** ❑ Lesson 3 **1LS2.c** ❑ Lesson 4 **1LS2.c** ❑ Lesson 5 **1LS2.c** ❑ Lesson 6 **1LS2.d**	
1IE4.0 Scientific progress is made by asking meaningful questions and conducting careful investigations. As a basis for understanding this concept and addressing the content in the other three strands, students should develop their own questions and perform investigations. **Date:** __/__/__	❑ Directed Inquiry **1LS2.c, 1IE4.b** ❑ Guided Inquiry **1LS2.c, 1IE4.a, 1IE4.b** ❑ Full Inquiry **1LS2.a, 1IE4.c**	
Chapter 6	**Lesson**	**Comments**
1ES3.0 Weather can be observed, measured, and described.	❑ Lesson 1 **1ES3.a, 1ES3.b** ❑ Lesson 2 **1ES3.a** ❑ Lesson 3 **1ES3.a** ❑ Lesson 4 **1ES3.c**	
1IE4.0 Scientific progress is made by asking meaningful questions and conducting careful investigations. As a basis for understanding this concept and addressing the content in the other three strands, students should develop their own questions and perform investigations. **Date:** __/__/__	❑ Directed Inquiry **1ES3.a, 1IE4.e** ❑ Guided Inquiry **1ES3.a, 1ES3.b, 1IE4.b, 1IE4.e**	
Chapter 7	**Lesson**	**Comments**
1ES3.0 Weather can be observed, measured, and described.	❑ Lesson 1 **1ES3.b** ❑ Lesson 2 **1ES3.b** ❑ Lesson 3 **1ES3.b** ❑ Lesson 4 **1ES3.b**	
1IE4.0 Scientific progress is made by asking meaningful questions and conducting careful investigations. As a basis for understanding this concept and addressing the content in the other three strands, students should develop their own questions and perform investigations. **Date:** __/__/__	❑ Directed Inquiry **1ES3.b, 1IE4.a, 1IE4.b** ❑ Guided Inquiry **1ES3.a, 1ES3.b, 1IE4.b** ❑ Full Inquiry **1ES3.c, 1IE4.b**	

Date: __/__/__

GRAPHIC ORGANIZER 1

Use Context Clues

GRAPHIC ORGANIZER 2

Put Things in Order

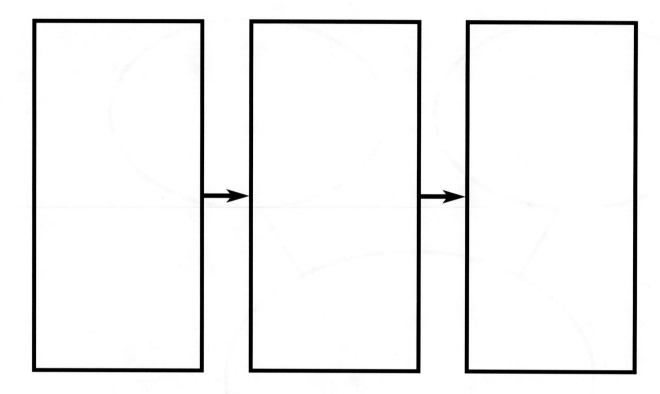

GRAPHIC ORGANIZER 3

Relate Prior Knowledge

Tell what I know.

GRAPHIC ORGANIZER 4

Predict

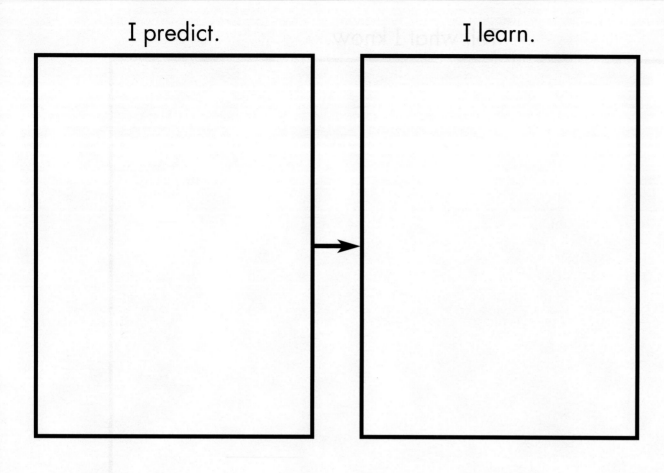

I predict.

I learn.

GRAPHIC ORGANIZER 5

Ask and Answer Questions

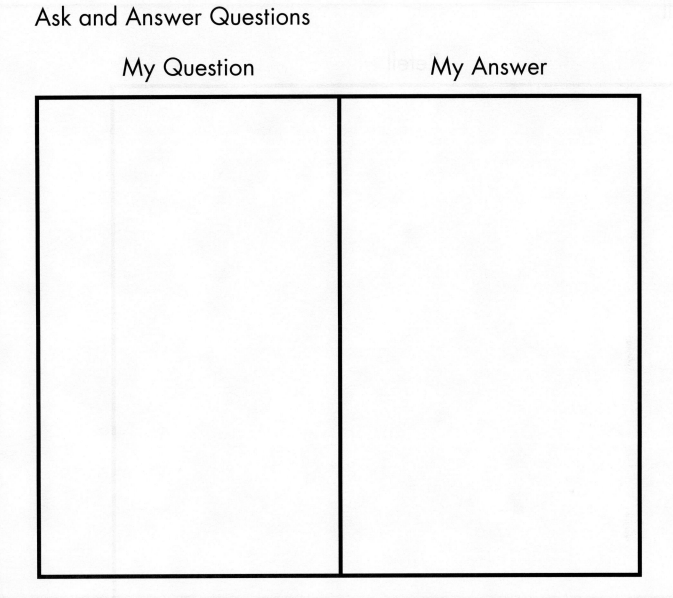

My Question | My Answer

GRAPHIC ORGANIZER 6

Retell

Retell

GRAPHIC ORGANIZER 7

K-W-L Chart

What We **K**now	What We **W**ant to Know	What We **L**earned

SCOPE AND SEQUENCE

Unit A Physical Sciences

KIE4.0 1IE4.0 2IE4.0 3IE5.0 4IE6.0 5IE6.0	Scientific progress is made by asking meaningful questions and conducting careful investigations. As a basis for understanding this concept and addressing the content in the other three strands, students should develop their own questions and perform investigations.

Unit B Life Sciences

KIE4.0 1IE4.0 2IE4.0 3IE5.0 4IE6.0 5IE6.0	Scientific progress is made by asking meaningful questions and conducting careful investigations. As a basis for understanding this concept and addressing the content in the other three strands, students should develop their own questions and perform investigations.

GRADE K

KPS1.0 Properties of materials can be observed, measured, and predicted.

Chapter 1 Objects All Around

Chapter 2 Water

KLS2.0 Different types of plants and animals inhabit the earth.

Chapter 3 Learning About Plants and Animals

Chapter 4 Plants and Animal Parts

GRADE 1

1PS1.0 Materials come in different forms (states), including solids, liquids, and gases.

Chapter 1 Observing Solids, Liquids, and Gases

Chapter 2 Changing Solids, Liquids, and Gases

1LS2.0 Plants and animals meet their needs in different ways.

Chapter 3 Needs of Plants and Animals

Chapter 4 Environments

Chapter 5 Plants and Animals Living Together

GRADE 2

2PS1.0 The motion of objects can be observed and measured.

Chapter 1 Forces and Motion

Chapter 2 Sound

2LS2.0 Plants and animals have predictable life cycles.

Chapter 3 Plants and Animals in Their Environment

Chapter 4 Animal Life Cycles

Chapter 5 All About Plants

GRADE 3

3PS1.0 Energy and matter have multiple forms and can be changed from one form to another.
3PS2.0 Light has a source and travels in a direction.

Chapter 1 Energy

Chapter 2 Light

Chapter 3 Matter

3LS3.0 Adaptations in physical structure or behavior may improve an organism's chance for survival.

Chapter 4 Living in Different Environments

Chapter 5 Living Things in a World of Change

GRADE 4

4PS1.0 Electricity and magnetism are related effects that have many useful applications in everyday life.

Chapter 1 Electricity

Chapter 2 Magnetism

4LS2.0 All organisms need energy and matter to live and grow.
4LS3.0 Living organisms depend on one another and on their environment for survival.

Chapter 3 Flow of Energy and Matter

Chapter 4 Ecosystems

Chapter 5 Interactions in Ecosystems

GRADE 5

5PS1.0 Elements and their combinations account for all the varied types of matter in the world.

Chapter 1 Building Blocks of Matter

Chapter 2 Changes in Matter

5LS2.0 Plants and animals have structures for respiration, digestion, waste disposal, and transport of materials.

Chapter 3 Basic Structures of Organisms

Chapter 4 Human Body Systems

Unit C Earth Sciences

KIE4.0 1IE4.0 2IE4.0 3IE5.0 4IE6.0 5IE6.0	Scientific progress is made by asking meaningful questions and conducting careful investigations. As a basis for understanding this concept and addressing the content in the other three strands, students should develop their own questions and perform investigations.

KES3.0 Earth is composed of land, air, and water.

Chapter 5 **Our Land, Air, and Water**

Chapter 6 **Weather**

Chapter 7 **Earth's Resources**

1ES3.0 Weather can be observed, measured, and described.

Chapter 6 **Observing Weather**

Chapter 7 **Seasons**

2ES3.0 Earth is made of materials that have distinct properties and provide resources for human activities.

Chapter 6 **Rocks and Soil**

Chapter 7 **Fossils and Dinosaurs**

3ES4.0 Objects in the sky move in regular and predictable patterns.

Chapter 6 **Objects in Space**

Chapter 7 **Patterns in the Sky**

4ES4.0 The properties of rocks and minerals reflect the processes that formed them.

4ES5.0 Waves, wind, water, and ice shape and reshape Earth's land surface.

Chapter 6 **Minerals and Rocks**

Chapter 7 **Our Changing Earth**

5ES3.0 Water on Earth moves between the oceans and land through the processes of evaporation and condensation.

5ES4.0 Energy from the Sun heats Earth unevenly, causing air movements that result in changing weather patterns.

5ES5.0 The solar system consists of planets and other bodies that orbit the Sun in predictable paths.

Chapter 5 **Water on Earth**

Chapter 6 **Weather**

Chapter 7 **The Solar System**

Focus on Earth Sciences

 GRADE 6

6IE7.0 Scientific progress is made by asking meaningful questions and conducting careful investigations. As a basis for understanding this concept and addressing the content in the other three strands, students should develop their own questions and perform investigations.

6ES2.0 Topography is reshaped by the weathering of rock and soil and by the transportation and deposition of sediment.

6ES3.a Students know energy can be carried from one place to another by heat flow or by waves, including water, light and sound waves, or by moving objects.

6ES6.0 Sources of energy and materials differ in amounts, distribution, usefulness, and the time required for their formation.

Chapter 1 **Introduction to Earth Science**

Chapter 2 **Weathering and Soil**

Chapter 3 **Erosion and Deposition**

6ES1.0 Plate tectonics accounts for important features of Earth's surface and major geologic events.

6ES2.0 Topography is reshaped by the weathering of rock and soil and by the transportation and deposition of sediment.

6ES3.c Students know heat flows in solids by conduction (which involves no flow of matter) and in fluids by conduction and by convection (which involves flow of matter).

Chapter 4 **Plate Tectonics**

Chapter 5 **Earthquakes**

Chapter 6 **Volcanoes**

6ES3.d Students know heat energy is also transferred between objects by radiation (radiation can travel through space).

6ES4.0 Many phenomena on Earth's surface are affected by the transfer of energy through radiation and convection currents.

Chapter 7 **The Atmosphere**

Chapter 8 **Weather**

Chapter 9 **Climate and Climate Change**

6ES3.b Students know that when fuel is consumed, most of the energy released becomes heat energy.

6ES5.0 Organisms in ecosystems exchange energy and nutrients among themselves and with the environment.

6ES6.0 Sources of energy and materials differ in amounts, distribution, usefulness, and the time required for their formation.

Chapter 10 **Ecosystems**

Chapter 11 **Living Resources**

Chapter 12 **Energy and Material Resources**

SUPPORT FOR ENGLISH LANGUAGE DEVELOPMENT

Science Content for English Language Learners

California English Language Development (ELD) standards are identified at point of use and summarized here for convenience.

English-Language Development Standards	Page number
LSB1 **ELD Listening and Speaking** Begin to speak a few words or sentences by using some English phonemes and rudimentary English grammatical forms (e.g., single words or phrases).	9, 17, 43, 45, 137, 185
LSB2 **ELD Listening and Speaking** Answer simple questions with one- to two-word responses.	39, 47, 133, 139, 141, 145, 149, 187, 207, 211, 213, 215
LSB3 **ELD Listening and Speaking** Respond to simple directions and questions by using physical actions and other means of nonverbal communication (e.g., matching objects, pointing to an answer, drawing pictures).	13, 21, 51, 79, 107, 111, 115, 181, 189
RB4 **ELD Reading** Demonstrate comprehension of simple vocabulary with an appropriate action.	83, 87
RB7 **ELD Reading** Respond orally to stories read aloud, using physical actions and other means of nonverbal communication (e.g., matching objects, pointing to an answer, drawing pictures).	19
RB9 **ELD Reading** Draw pictures from one's own experience related to a story or topic (e.g., community in social studies).	103
LSEI2 **ELD Listening and Speaking** Ask and answer questions by using phrases or simple sentences.	13, 39, 115, 139, 207, 211, 213, 215
REI4 **ELD Reading** Read simple vocabulary, phrases, and sentences independently.	141
REI8 **ELD Reading** Draw and label pictures related to a story topic or one's own experience.	79, 133
REI11 **ELD Reading** Draw logical inferences from a story read aloud.	149
REI12 **ELD Reading** Respond orally to factual comprehension questions about stories by answering in simple sentences.	87
WEI3 **ELD Writing** Write one to two simple sentences (e.g., "I went to the park").	83, 107
LSI1 **ELD Listening and Speaking** Ask and answer instructional questions by using simple sentences.	137, 185, 187
LSI2 **ELD Listening and Speaking** Listen attentively to stories and information and identify important details and concepts by using both verbal and nonverbal responses.	47
LSI3 **ELD Listening and Speaking** Make oneself understood when speaking by using consistent standard English grammatical forms and sounds; however, some rules may not be followed (e.g., third-person singular, male and female pronouns).	45, 145
LSI4 **ELD Listening and Speaking** Participate in social conversations with peers and adults on familiar topics by asking and answering questions and soliciting information.	9, 189
RI12 **ELD Reading** Write captions or phrases for drawings related to a story.	19
WI1 **ELD Writing** Write short narrative stories that include the elements of setting and characters.	103
WI2 **ELD Writing** Produce independent writing that is understood when read but may include inconsistent use of standard grammatical forms.	51
WI4 **ELD Writing** Write simple sentences appropriate for language arts and other content areas (e.g., math, science, social studies).	17, 43, 111, 181
WI5 **ELD Writing** Write a friendly letter of a few lines.	21

BEGINNING

EARLY INTERMEDIATE

INTERMEDIATE

English-Language Development Standards	Page number
LSEA3 **ELD Listening and Speaking** Make oneself understood when speaking by using consistent standard English grammatical forms, sounds, intonation, pitch, and modulation but may make random errors.	181
LSEA6 **ELD Listening and Speaking** Ask and answer instructional questions with more extensive supporting elements (e.g., "Which part of the story was the most important?").	9
REA7 **ELD Reading** Read stories and orally respond to them by answering factual comprehension questions about cause-and-effect relationships.	87
REA8 **ELD Reading** Track (move sequentially from sound to sound) and represent changes in simple syllables and words with two and three sounds as one sound is added, substituted, omitted, shifted, or repeated (e.g., vowel-consonant, consonant-vowel, or consonant-vowel-consonant).	19
REA10 **ELD Reading** Read stories and texts from content areas and respond orally to them by restating facts and details to clarify ideas.	137
REA13 **ELD Reading** Read a story and identify the beginning, middle, and end.	139
WEA1 **ELD Writing** Write short narratives that include elements of setting, characters, and events.	189
WEA2 **ELD Writing** Proceed through the writing process to write short paragraphs that maintain a consistent focus.	51
WEA3 **ELD Writing** Use complex vocabulary and sentences appropriate for language arts and other content areas (e.g., math, science, social studies).	13, 141, 145, 187
LSA1 **ELD Listening and Speaking** Listen attentively to stories and information on new topics and identify both orally and in writing key details and concepts.	103, 133
LSA3 **ELD Listening and Speaking** Negotiate and initiate social conversations by questioning, restating, soliciting information, and paraphrasing the communication of others.	43
LSA4 **ELD Listening and Speaking** Consistently use appropriate ways of speaking and writing that vary according to the purpose, audience, and subject matter.	107
RA6 **ELD Reading** Prepare an oral or a written summary by using various comprehension strategies (e.g., generate and respond to questions, draw inferences, compare information from several sources) with literature and content area texts.	83, 115, 149
WA1 **ELD Writing** Write short narratives that include examples of writing appropriate for language arts and other content areas (e.g., math, science, social studies).	21, 39, 45, 207, 211, 213, 215
WA2 **ELD Writing** Write short narratives that describe the setting, characters, objects, and events.	17, 47
WA4 **ELD Writing** Proceed through the writing process to write clear and coherent sentences and paragraphs that maintain a consistent focus.	79, 111
WA5 **ELD Writing** Use complete sentences and correct word order.	185

EARLY ADVANCED

ADVANCED

TABLE OF EVIDENCE

Chapter 1 Observing Solids, Liquids, and Gases

		1PS1.a	1PS1.b	1IE4.a	1IE4.b	1IE4.c	1IE4.d	1IE4.e
Directed Inquiry Explore **What can change shape?** p. 6	10 min	•		•				
1 What is a property? pp. 8–11	30 min	•						
2 What is a solid? pp. 12–15	30 min	•						
3 What is a liquid? pp. 16–17	20 min	•						
4 What is a gas? pp. 18–19	20 min	•						
5 How are solids, liquids, and gases different? pp. 20–21	20 min	•						
Guided Inquiry Investigate **How much space does a liquid take up?** pp. 24–25	15 min	•			•			

Chapter 2 Changing Solids, Liquids, and Gases

		1PS1.a	1PS1.b	1IE4.a	1IE4.b	1IE4.c	1IE4.d	1IE4.e
Directed Inquiry Explore **How can mixing change things?** p. 36	10 min		•		•			
1 How can things change? pp. 38–41	30 min		•					
2 What properties of things can change? pp. 42–43	20 min		•					
3 What changes when things are mixed? pp. 44–45	20 min		•					
4 How can cooling and heating change things? pp. 46–49	30 min		•					
5 What things can not change back? pp. 50–51	20 min		•					
Guided Inquiry Investigate **How can ice change when it melts?** pp. 54–55	15 min		•		•			
Full Inquiry Experiment **What happens when air is heated?** pp. 62–63	20 min		•	•	•			

		1LS2.a	1LS2.b	1LS2.c	1LS2.d	1LS2.e	1IE4.a	1IE4.b	1IE4.c	1IE4.d	1IE4.e

Chapter 3 Needs of Plants and Animals

Directed Inquiry **Explore Do plants need water?** p. 76	15 min		•					•			
1 **What do plants need?** pp. 78–81	30 min		•								
2 **How do plants get what they need?** pp. 82–85	30 min				•						
3 **What do animals need?** pp. 86–87	20 min		•								
Guided Inquiry **Investigate Do plants need light?** pp. 90–91	15 min		•		•			•			

Chapter 4 Environments

Directed Inquiry **Explore Where do animals live?** p. 100	10 min	•					•				
1 **What is an environment?** pp. 102–105	30 min	•									
2 **What lives in a forest?** pp. 106–109	30 min	•									
3 **What lives in an ocean?** pp. 110–113	30 min	•									
4 **What lives in a desert?** pp. 114–117	30 min	•									
Guided Inquiry **Investigate How do some desert leaves hold water?** pp. 120–121	20 min	•					•	•			

Chapter 5 Plants and Animals Living Together

Directed Inquiry **Explore What do animals eat for food?** p. 130	10 min			•			•				
1 **How do plants and animals need one another?** pp. 132–135	30 min			•							
2 **How do animals help spread seeds?** pp. 136–137	20 min			•							
3 **What is a food chain?** pp. 138–139	20 min			•							
4 **How do living things get food in a desert?** pp. 140–143	30 min			•							
5 **How do living things get food in a marsh?** pp. 144–147	30 min			•							
6 **What do animals eat?** pp. 148–151	30 min				•						
Guided Inquiry **Investigate How can you make a model of a food chain?** pp. 154–155	20 min			•				•	•		
Full Inquiry **Experiment How can color help mice stay hidden from hawks?** pp. 164–165	20 min	•								•	

Chapter 6 Observing Weather

		1ES3.a	1ES3.b	1ES3.c	1IE4.a	1IE4.b	1IE4.c	1IE4.d	1IE4.e
Directed Inquiry Explore **What does a wind vane measure?** p. 178	15 min	•							•
1 **What is weather?** pp. 180–183	30 min	•	•						
2 **How hot or cold is the weather?** pp. 184–185	20 min	•							
3 **How can you measure rain?** pp. 186–187	20 min	•							
4 **What does the Sun do?** pp. 188–189	20 min			•					
Guided Inquiry Investigate **How much rain falls?** pp. 192–193	15 min	•	•			•			•

Chapter 7 Seasons

		1ES3.a	1ES3.b	1ES3.c	1IE4.a	1IE4.b	1IE4.c	1IE4.d	1IE4.e
Directed Inquiry Explore **What is the weather like in different seasons?** p. 204	10 min		•		•	•			
1 **What is a season?** pp. 206–209	30 min		•						
2 **What is the weather like in summer?** pp. 210–211	20 min		•						
3 **What is the weather like in fall?** pp. 212–213	20 min		•						
4 **What is the weather like in winter?** pp. 214–215	20 min		•						
Guided Inquiry Investigate **How does the temperature change from day to day?** pp. 218–219	15 min	•	•				•		
Full Inquiry Experiment **Does the Sun warm land or water faster?** pp. 226–227	25 min				•		•		

CALIFORNIA SCIENCE STANDARDS CHECKLIST

STANDARD SET 1. Physical Sciences

1PS1.0 Materials come in different forms (states), including solids, liquids, and gases. As a basis for understanding this concept:

	Introductory	Reinforcing ✓ = Checkpoint/ Lesson Review Questions	Summative
1PS1.a Students know solids, liquids, and gases have different properties.	pp. **6**, 8, 9, **12, 16, 18**	pp. **10, 11, 13,** 14, **17, 19**	pp. **20, 21,** 24, 25, **26, 28, 29, 48, 58, 61, 64, 67, 68**
1PS1.b Students know the properties of substances can change when the substances are mixed, cooled, or heated.	36, 38, **39**	**40, 41, 42, 43, 44, 45, 46, 48, 49**	50, 51, 54, 55, **56, 58, 59,** 60, **61,** 62, 63, **64, 69, 70**

Instructional time allotment for learning the content of each standard is provided on Lesson Planning Guides (pp. 3a–3b, 33a–33b).

CALIFORNIA SCIENCE STANDARDS CHECKLIST

STANDARD SET 2. Life Sciences

1LS2.0 Plants and animals meet their needs in different ways. As a basis for understanding this concept:

	Introductory	Reinforcing ✓ = Checkpoint/ Lesson Review Questions	Summative
1LS2.a Students know different plants and animals inhabit different kinds of environments and have external features that help them thrive in different kinds of places.	pp. 100, 102, **103, 104**	pp. 105, 106, 107, 108, 109, **110,** 111, 112, 113, 114, 115, 116, 117	pp. 120, 121, **122, 124, 125,** 144, 145, 160, 161, **163,** 164, 165, 166, **170, 171**
1LS2.b Students know both plants and animals need water, animals need food, and plants need light.	**76, 78,** 79, **80**	81, **87**	**90, 91, 92, 94,** 138, **163, 169**
1LS2.c Students know animals eat plants or other animals for food and may also use plants or even other animals for shelter and nesting.	130, 132, **133**	**134,** 135, **138,** 139, 140, 141, 142, 143, 148, 150	144, 145, 146, 147, 154, 155, **156,** 158, 159, **163,** 164, 165, **171, 172**
1LS2.d Students know how to infer what animals eat from the shapes of their teeth (e.g., sharp teeth: eats meat; flat teeth: eats plants).	148	**149, 150, 151**	**156, 158, 172**
1LS2.e Students know roots are associated with the intake of water and soil nutrients and green leaves are associated with making food from sunlight.	82	**83, 84, 85**	90, 91, **92, 94, 95**

Instructional time allotment for learning the content of each standard is provided on Lesson Planning Guides (pp. 73a–73b, 97a–97b, 127a–127b).

STANDARD SET 3. Earth Sciences

1ES3.0 Weather can be observed, measured, and described. As a basis for understanding this concept:

	Introductory	Reinforcing ✓ = Checkpoint/ Lesson Review Questions	Summative
1ES3.a Students know how to use simple tools (e.g., thermometer, wind vane) to measure weather conditions and record changes from day to day and across the seasons.	pp. **178, 183**	pp.184, **185,** 186, **187**	pp. **192, 193, 194, 196, 197,** 218, 219, **225, 226, 231, 232**
1ES3.b Students know that the weather changes from day to day but that trends in temperature or of rain (or snow) tend to be predictable during a season.	180, **181, 184,** 204, 206, **207**	208, 209, 210, 211, 212, 213, 214, 215	**194, 196, 197,** 218, 219, **220, 222, 223, 225,** 228, **233, 234**
1ES3.c Students know the sun warms the land, air, and water.	188	**189**	**194, 196, 197, 226, 227, 232**

Instructional time allotment for learning the content of each standard is provided on Lesson Planning Guides (pp. 175a–175b, 201a–201b).

CALIFORNIA SCIENCE STANDARDS CHECKLIST

STANDARD SET 4. Investigation and Experimentation

1IE4.0 Scientific progress is made by asking meaningful questions and conducting careful investigations. As a basis for understanding this concept and addressing the content in the other three strands, students should develop their own questions and perform investigations. Students will:

1IE4.a Draw pictures that portray some features of the thing being described.	pp. **63, 100, 120, 121, 154, 155, 204**
1IE4.b Record observations and data with pictures, numbers, or written statements.	**6, 24, 25, 36, 54, 55, 63,** 76, **91, 120, 121, 130, 154, 155, 192, 193,** 204, **218, 219, 227**
1IE4.c Record observations on a bar graph.	**52, 53, 165**
1IE4.d Describe the relative position of objects by using two references (e.g., above and next to, below and left of).	**13, 22, 23, 57**
1IE4.e Make new observations when discrepancies exist between two descriptions of the same object or phenomenon.	**178, 193**

Instructional time allotment for learning the content of each standard is provided on Lesson Planning Guides (pp. 3a–3b, 33a–33b, 73a–73b, 97a–97b, 127a–127b, 175a–175b, 201a–201b).

Glossary

The glossary uses letters and signs to show how words are pronounced. The mark ′ is placed after a syllable with a primary or heavy accent. The mark ′ is placed after a syllable with a secondary or lighter accent.

To hear these words pronounced, listen to the AudioText CD.

Pronunciation Key

a in hat	ō in open	sh in she
ā in age	ȯ in all	th in thin
â in care	ô in order	ŦH in then
ä in far	oi in oil	zh in measure
e in let	ou in out	ə = a in about
ē in equal	u in cup	ə = e in taken
ėr in term	ù in put	ə = i in pencil
i in it	ü in rule	ə = o in lemon
ī in ice	ch in child	ə = u in circus
o in hot	ng in long	

air (er) A gas that plants and animals need to live. You cannot see **air.** (page 80)

animal (an′ə məl) A living thing that moves about. A giraffe is an **animal** with a long neck. (page 105)

answer questions (an′sər kwes′shənz) Give responses to questions. You can **answer questions** about what you have read. (page 179)

EM5

ask questions (ask kwes′shənz)
What you can do to find out
something you do not know. You
can **ask questions** about what
you want to learn before you
read. (page 179)

B

balance (bal′ əns) A tool that can
compare the weights of objects.
The **balance** compares the
weights of the ball and the toy
bear. (page 14)

blubber (blub′ər) The fat of a
whale. **Blubber** keeps a whale
warm in the ocean. (page 113)

C

classify (klas′ə fī) To put things
that are alike in groups. You can
classify animals by where they
live. (page 100)

claws (klôwz) The sharp, curved nails of some animals. The bear uses its **claws** to climb trees. (page 108)

collect data (kə lekt′ dā′tə) To gather information. You **collect data** when you record your observations in pictures or writing. (page 76)

communicate (ke myü′nə kāt) To use words or pictures to share information. You **communicate** when you tell what you did first, next, and last. (page 33)

container (kən tā′ nər) An object that holds things inside it. A liquid takes the shape of its **container.** (page 17)

context clues (kon′tekst klüz) Pictures or words that help you understand what you are reading. The picture can give you **context clues** about how blocks are different. (page 7)

cool (kül) To lower the temperature of something. **Cooling** changes melted wax into solid crayons. (page 41)

D

desert (dez′ ərt) An environment that is very dry. Many plants and animals live in a **desert.** (page 114)

dissolve (di zolv′) Spread throughout a liquid. Salt **dissolves** when it is mixed with water. (page 45)

EM8

E

environment (en vī′ rən mənt)
A place where plants and
animals live. An **environment**
gives plants and animals what
they need. (page 103)

estimate (es′tə māt) To make a
careful guess about the size or
amount of something. You can
estimate air temperature by
how warm or cool it feels. (p. xii)

evaporate (i vap′ə rāt′) Change
from a liquid to a gas. Heat
from the sunlight causes water to
evaporate. (page 48)

experiment (ek sper′ə mənt)
use scientific methods to test
a hypothesis. You can do an
experiment to find out what
happens when air is heated.
(page 62)

EM9

explore (ek splôr′) To study science in a hands-on manner. You can **explore** the differences between solids, liquids, and gases. (page 6)

fair test (fâr test) To make sure only one thing is changed in an experiment. You plan a **fair test** in an experiment when you choose the one thing that you will change. (page 226)

fall (fôl) The season that comes after summer. **Fall** is cooler than summer. (page 212)

float (flōt) A round part of a Kelp plant that lifts the plant up in the water. **Floats** help a Kelp plant get the sunlight it needs (page 110)

EM10

fog (fog) A cloud near the ground. Some summer nights have **fog.** (page 211)

food (füd) Something animals need to live. The bear eats a fish for **food.** (page 87)

food chain (füd chān) The way food passes from one living thing to another. Plants and animals depend on each other through **food chains.** (page 131)

forest (fôr'ist) An environment that has many trees and other plants. Many animals live in a **forest.** (page 106)

freeze (frēz) Change from a liquid to a solid. Water **freezes** when it gets very cold. (page 46)

fur (fėr) The covering on some animals that is like hair. A sea otter has thick **fur** to keep warm in the ocean. (page 112)

EM11

G

gas (gas) Something that takes the shape and size of its container. Air is a **gas.** (page 18)

gills (gilz) A body part a fish uses to get air. The fish has **gills** to breathe in water. (page 111)

H

heat (hēt) To increase the temperature of something. **Heating** changes solid wax into a liquid. (page 40)

hooves (hŭvz) The hard parts of the feet of some animals. A sheep has **hooves** to climb on rocks. (page 104)

EM12

hypothesis (hī poth′ə sis) A statement of one possible way to solve a problem or answer a question. You make and test a **hypothesis** to do an experiment. (page 62)

infer (in fėr) To use what you have learned or what you know to make a guess about something. You can **infer** what some animals eat by the shape of their teeth. (page 130)

insect (in′sekt) A small animal that has six legs and a hard covering. Some **insects** eat plants. (page 162)

interpret data (in tėr′prit dā′tə)

To use the information you have
collected to solve problems
or answer questions. You can
interpret the **data** you collect to
find out what they mean.
(page 121)

investigate (in ves′tə gāt)

To solve a problem or answer
a question by following steps.
You can **investigate** how
much space a liquid takes up.
(page 24)

 L

leaves (lēvz) The parts of a plant
that make food for the plant.
Green **leaves** use sunlight, air,
and water to make food.
(page 84)

light (līt) Something a plant needs
to live. Plants may get **light** from
the Sun. (page 80)

EM14

liquid (lik′wid) Something that takes the shape of its container and has its own amount or size. You can pour a **liquid.** (page 16)

living (liv′ing) Things that are alive, grow, and change. Plants and animals are **living** things. (page 79)

marsh (marsh) A wetland environment. Many plants and animals live in a **marsh.** (page 144)

material (mə tir′ē əl) What something is made of or used for. A tissue, a paper towel, and a piece of cloth are different **materials.** (page 32)

EM15

measure (mezh′ər) To use a tool to compare the size or amount of something. You can use a thermometer to **measure** the temperature of air. (page 218)

melt (melt) Change from a solid into a liquid. Solid wax **melts** when it is heated. (page 42)

mix (miks) To put two or more things together. **Mixing** blue and yellow paint changes the color to green. (page 42)

model (mod′l) A drawing or object that represents something else. You can use pictures to make a **model** food chain. (page 154)

 N

nest (nest) A shelter that some animals build. Some birds build **nests** in trees. (page 134)

EM16

nutrients (nü′trē ənt) Materials that living things need. Plants can get **nutrients** from the soil. (page 83)

observe (əb zėrv′) To use your senses to find out about an object. You can observe what you see, hear, smell, taste, or touch. (page 4)

ocean (ō′shən) An environment that is a large body of salt water. Many animals and plants live in an ocean. (p. 110)

plant (plant) A living thing that cannot move around on its own. This **plant** grows in a forest. (page 106)

EM17

predict (pri dikt′) Tell what you think will happen next. You can **predict** what will happen if plants do not get light. (page 90)

property (prop′ər tē) Something that you can observe with your senses. The size of an object is one of its **properties.** (page 9)

put things in order (pu̇t thingz in ôr′dər) Decide what is first, next, and last. You can **put** the **things** that happen in a science activity **in order.** (page 37)

 R

rain gauge (rān gāj) A weather tool to measure the amount of rain. The numbers show how much rain falls into a **rain gauge.** (page 187)

EM18

relate prior knowledge
(ri lāt′ prō′ər nol′ij) To use what you already know to understand something new. You can **relate** your **prior knowledge** about animals to what you are learning now. (page 77)

retell (rē tel′) To tell what you learned in your own words. You can **retell** the main idea of a story. (page 205)

root (rüt) Part of a plant that holds the plant in the ground. **Roots** take in water and nutrients from the soil. (page 83)

season (sē′zn) A time of year. Spring, summer, fall, and winter are the four **seasons.** (page 207)

shape (shāp) the way something looks. The ball has a circle **shape.** (page 10)

shelter (shel'tər) A safe place for animals to live. Some animals build nests for **shelter.** (page 134)

size (sīz) How big something is. The red car is bigger in **size** than the purple car. (page 12)

solid (sol'id) Something that has its own shape and size. A wooden block is a **solid.** (page 12)

spring (spring) The season that comes after winter. Temperatures get warmer in **spring.** (page 208)

summer (sum'ər) The season that comes after spring. **Summer** may be very dry. (page 210)

Sun (sun) A big ball of hot gas that shines light on Earth. Light from the **Sun** warms the land, water, and air. (page 189)

EM20

temperature (tem′per ə chər)
How hot or cold something
is. You can measure the
temperature of air. (page 184)

thermometer (thər mom′ ə tər)
A tool that measures temperature.
The numbers on a **thermometer**
show the temperature.
(page 185)

water (wô′tər) Liquid that plants,
and animals need to live. The
bear is drinking **water.**
(page 87)

weather (weᴛʜ′ ər) What it is like
outside. **Weather** changes from
day to day. (page 180)

weight (wāt) How heavy an object feels when you pick it up. A balance can compare the **weights** of objects (page 114).

wind (wind) Moving air. The **wind** is blowing hard. (page 182)

wind vane (wind vān) A weather tool that tells which way the wind is blowing. A **wind vane** points into the wind. (page 183)

winter (win′tər) The season that comes after fall. **Winter** is the coldest season. (page 214)

Index

Page numbers after a *p* refer to a photograph or drawing. Page numbers after a *c* refer to a chart, graph, or diagram. Boldface page numbers indicate pages in the Teacher's Edition. Other page numbers indicate pages in the Student Edition that are reproduced in the Teacher's Edition.

Credits

(for Student Edition)

Illustrations

27, 57, 68–69, 87, 115, 149, 172, 183, 207, 231 Kathie Kelleher; 32 Laura Ovresat; 44 Big Sesh Studios; 88 Alan Barnard

Photographs

Every effort has been made to secure permission and provide appropriate credit for photographic material. The publisher deeply regrets any omission and pledges to correct errors called to its attention in subsequent editions.

Unless otherwise acknowledged, all photographs are the property of Scott Foresman, a division of Pearson Education.

Photo locators denoted as follows: Top (T), Center (C), Bottom (B), Left (L), Right (R), Background (Bkgd).

3 Getty Images; 4 Adrian Myers/©AFP/Getty Images; 6 ©Rob Van Petten/Taxi/Getty Images; 8 (TL) ©DK Images, (Bkgd) Adrian Myers/©AFP/Getty Images; 10 Hemera Technologies; 13 ©DK Images; 28 (BL) NASA Image Exchange, (BL, Bkgd) NASA; 30 (TL) Corbis, (BR) ©ESA/PLI/Corbis, (Bkgd) ©Photographer's Choice/Getty Images, (B) ©JPL/Cornell/ NASA, (CL) NASA, (BR) ©NASA/Corbis; 36 ©Boden/ Ledingham/Masterfile Corporation; 37 ©Andy Crawford/DK Images; 38 (TL) Getty Images, (Bkgd) ©Gale Zucker; 39 (TR, CR) ©Gale Zucker; 46 (TR) Martin Cameron/©DK Images, (TR) Rita Maas/©AFP/Getty Images, (Bkgd) Dave King/©DK Images; 47 ©photolibrary pty. ltd./Index Open; 60 Courtesy David Smith Photography; 60 (Bkgd) Getty Images, (TR) ©James L. Amos/Corbis; 66 (Bkgd) Getty Images, (TR) ©DK Images, (CL) Digital Vision; 71 (TR) ©DK Images, (Bkgd) ©Paul Nicklen/National Geographic Image Collection; 72 (BL) JPL/ NASA, (CL) ©Cris Cordeiro/PhotoLibrary, (BL) ©Craig Tuttle/ Corbis, (TL) ©Neil Fletcher and Matthew Ward/DK Images; 73 Getty Images; 74 (TL) ©DK Images, (BL, BC, BR) Matthew Ward/©DK Images; 75 (TR) Corbis, ©Paul Nicklen/National Geographic Image Collection, (TL) ©Runk/Schoenberger/Grant Heilman Photography; 76 ©DK Images; 78 (Bkgd) ©Anup Shah/Nature Picture Library, (B) ©Royalty-Free/Corbis; 79 (TC) Digital Vision, (Bkgd) ©Tom Brakefield/Corbis; 88 (Bkgd) ©Jochem D. Wijnands/Getty Images, (TL) ©Paul Chesley/ Getty Images; 96 (Bkgd) ©W. Perry Conway/Corbis, (Bkgd) ©John Elk III/Getty Images, (TR) ©ZSSD/Minden Pictures, (BL) ©Konrad Wothe/Minden Pictures; 97 (TR) ©Jeremy Thomas/Natural Visions, (BR) ©Taxi/Getty Images; 98 (TL) ©DK Images, (BL) ©Kevin Schafer/Corbis, (Bkgd) ©Kevin Schafer/Corbis; 99 (TR) ©Art Wolfe/Getty Images, (CR) ©DK Images; 100 (TL) ©Tom & Pat Leeson/Photo Researchers, Inc., (BL) Peter Chadwick/©DK Images; 101 (CR) ©Tom & Pat Leeson/Photo Researchers, Inc., (TR) ©Theo Allofs/Zefa/ Corbis, (CR, BL) Getty Images, (Bkgd) ©John Warden/Getty Images; 102 (BL) © David Welling/Animals Animals/Earth Scenes, (Bkgd) ©Tom Brakefield/Corbis; 103 (TR) ©Galen Rowell/Corbis, (BR) ©John D. Cunningham /Visuals Unlimited; 104 ©Stone/Getty Images, (TR) Getty Images, (CR) ©Morse, Randy/Animals Animals/Earth Scenes, (BR) ©Flip Nicklin /Minden Pictures; 105 Digital Vision; 106 (TL) ©Morse, Randy/Animals Animals/Earth Scenes, (B) ©Lightwave Photography, Inc./Animals Animals/Earth Scenes; 107 (TR) ©Bill Coster/NHPA Limited, (C) ©Bob Cranston/Seapics; 108 (TL) ©Zig Leszczynski/Animals Animals/Earth Scenes, (TR) ©Doug Sokell/Visuals Unlimited, (CR) ©Karl Switak/ NHPA Limited; 109 ©Tom Bean/Corbis; 110 (TL) ©Gerlach Nature Photography /Animals Animals/Earth Scenes, (CL) ©David Kjaer/Nature Picture Library, (Bkgd) ©Daniel Heuclin /NHPA Limited; 111 ©Gerlach Nature Photography /Animals Animals/Earth Scenes; 114 ©Doug Sokell/Visuals Unlimited; 124 ©Joseph Sohm/ChromoSohm Inc./Corbis; 125 (TL) ©DK Images, (BR) ©Paul McCormick /Getty Images; 126 (TL) Corbis, (BL) ©Kenneth M. Highfill/Photo Researchers, Inc., (BC) ©Kennan Ward/Corbis, (BR) ©Stephen Dalton/NHPA Limited, (CR) ©Eric and David Hosking/Corbis; 127 (CR) Corbis, (TR) ©NHMPL/Getty Images, (Bkgd) ©Michael S. Quinton/Getty Images; 128 ©Smith, Scott W./Animals Animals/Earth Scenes; 129 ©Nature's Images/Photo Researchers, Inc., ©Mark Moffet/Minden Pictures, ©Karl Switak/NHPA Limited, (TL) Alan Williams/NHPA Limited, (Bkgd) ©Ron Sanford/Corbis; 132 (TL) Hemera Technologies, (TR) ©Michael & Patricia Fogden/Corbis, (BR) ©Raymond Mendez /Animals Animals/ Earth Scenes, (BR) ©John Sullivan and Monica Rua/Ribbit Photography; 134 (BL) ©John Sullivan and Monica Rua/Ribbit Photography, (CL) ©Nelson, Alan G./Animals Animals/Earth Scenes; 135 (CL) ©John Sullivan and Monica Rua/Ribbit Photography, (BR) © Raymond Mendez/Animals Animals/ Earth Scenes, (TR, Bkgd) ©Galen Rowell/Corbis; 136 (TL, BR) ©Robert Erwin/NHPA Limited; 138 (TL) ©Ron Austing/Frank Lane Picture Agency/Corbis, (BR) ©Joe MacDonald /Corbis; 139 (TR) ©Joe MacDonald /Corbis, (BR) ©Robert Erwin/NHPA Limited, (TR) ©Ron Austing/Frank Lane Picture Agency/Corbis; 140 ©Mark Moffet/Minden Pictures, ©Karl Switak/NHPA Limited; 141 (TL) Digital Vision, ©Nature's Images/Photo Researchers, Inc.; 143 ©Nature's Images/Photo Researchers, Inc., ©Mark Moffet/Minden Pictures, ©Karl Switak/NHPA Limited; 144 ©John Shaw/Tom Stack & Associates, Inc.; 145 (TL) ©John Gerlach/Visuals Unlimited, (TC) ©Tim Wright/ Corbis, (TC) ©William J. Weber/Visuals Unlimited, (TR) ©Taxi/Getty Images, (TR) ©Michael Sewell/Peter Arnold, Inc., (TL) ©DK Images, (TL) ©Michael & Patricia Fogden/Corbis; 148 ©S. Purdy Matthews/Stone/Getty Images; 152 (Bkgd) Map Resources, (B) ©Marian Bacon/Animals Animals/Earth Scenes, (B) Getty Images; 153 (TR) ©Andrew Syred/Photo Researchers, Inc., (T) ©Royalty-Free/Corbis; 154 (BL) ©Kate Bennett Mendz/ Animals Animals/Earth Scenes, (TR, TC, BC) Jerry Young/©DK Images, (BR, CR) ©Royalty-Free/Corbis; 162 Getty Images; 164 ©Ian Beames/Ecoscene/Corbis; 166 ©Ariel Skelley/ Masterfile Corporation; 167 ©Corbis; 168 ©Stockbyte/ Getty Images; 170 ©Stephen Beaudet/Corbis; 171 ©Robert Landau/Corbis; 173 ©Ron and Patty Thomas /Getty Images; 174 (Bkgd) Michael McQueen/Getty Images, (Bkgd) ©Morton Beebe/Corbis; 175 (TR, CR) Getty Images, (Bkgd) ©Richard Kaylin/Getty Images; 176 (TCL) ©Taxi/Getty Images, (Bkgd) ©The Image Bank/Getty Images; 177 (TL, TR) ©Bruce Peebles/ Corbis; 180 Getty Images, (BR) Corbis, (Bkgd) ©Royalty-Free/Corbis, (TR) Getty Images, (BL) ©Reuters/Corbis; 185 (TL, BC) Getty Images; 186 ©Taxi/Getty Images; 192 ©Marc Muench/Corbis; 193 (BR, TR) ©Zefa Visual Media/Corbis; 194 (TL) Hemera Technologies, (B) ©Royalty-Free/Corbis; 196 (TL) Hemera Technologies, Getty Images, (B) ©Royalty-Free/

Corbis; 197 ©Garry Blac/Masterfile Corporation; 198 (TL) Hemera Technologies, (BR) Panoramic Images; 199 ©Morton Beebe/Corbis; 200 (TL) ©John Mead/Photo Researchers, Inc., (B) ©Tony Freeman /PhotoEdit; 201 (T) ©George D. Lepp/ Corbis, (Bkgd) ©Timothy Laman/National Geographic Image Collection, (Bkgd) ©Wes Walker/Getty Images; 205 ©Tim Barnett/Getty Images; 218 ©Royalty-Free/Corbis; 224 (Bkgd) ©Bruce Wilson/Getty Images, (BR) ©Adrian Weinbrecht/Getty Images; 226 Getty Images; 226 ©Wides & Holl/Getty Images

Credits

(for Teacher's Edition)

Photographs

1 ©Charles Gupton/Corbis; 3 Getty Images; 33 ©Taxi/Getty Images; 71 ©Martin Ruegner/Getty Images; 73 (B) ©Bill Curtsinger/Getty Images, (Bkgd) ©Frans Lanting/Minden Pictures; 97 ©Norbert Wu/Minden Pictures; 127 ©Michael S. Quinton/Getty Images; 143 ©Nature's Images/Photo Researchers, Inc.; 173 ©Ron and Patty Thomas /Getty Images; 175 ©Richard Kaylin/Getty Images; 201 ©Wes Walker/ Getty Images

EM30